CW00747260

THE TALE OF TWO TABBY CATS

THE TALE OF TWO TABBY CATS

Delphine White

The Book Guild Ltd
Sussex, England

First published in Great Britain in 2001 by
The Book Guild Ltd
25 High Street,
Lewes, East Sussex
BN7 2LU

Typesetting in Baskerville by
Keyboard Services, Luton, Bedfordshire

Printed in Great Britain by
Bookcraft (Bath) Ltd, Avon

A catalogue record for this book is
available from the British Library

ISBN 1 85776 572 9

INTRODUCTION

This is the story of my two beautiful stray cats – Tibby and Tabby. They both came to my back door, but 14 years apart.

Tibby arrived in 1982 and Tabby (Tabitha) in 1996. Why they chose our house I do not know, but I find it incredible to think that it was just a coincidence. Both were tabbies, both female, but each had a very different temperament. Tibby would scratch and swear if we upset her, but would sit on my lap for hours. Tabby does not like being held or cuddled, but very rarely has her claws out. We can only put their individual behaviour down to the kind of treatment they received before they came to us.

To someone like myself who had never owned a cat, they taught me everything there is to know about living in harmony with a cat: which chair was their favourite so beware; which place got the sun in the morning, or benefited from the heat emanating from the radiators, or how to disappear when it was time for a tablet; how to wheedle tasty bits of steak or chicken from the Master of the house when the humans were eating and how to get an extra helping of Whiskas. All a cat asks for is food and love, in that order, and for the owner, he or she, to be the willing slave of the adored cat.

Nine Lives and One More is the true story of Tibby and her life with us. There are some passages that are mere flights of imagination on my part, but for the rest of the story it is an account of the day-to-day happenings of a little stray cat, who found a new home and the love of a new family. We learnt a great deal from her, especially my husband who was not used to the ways of a cat, and tried to teach her to be more like a dog. You can guess who won that battle.

Ghost of a Cat is the story of our second little stray, Tabby, but with more than a little imagination on my part in the storyline. But then who can say where reality ends and fantasy takes over in the mind of the beholder? She taught us a lot more about the wisdom of the feline mind and although I do not believe in talking to a cat in 'cat language', I know she understands every word I say and, what is even more strange, she can make herself understood by us. Of that I have no doubt.

So, dear reader, if you are a cat lover, I am sure you will see something of your own pets in either of the stories. If you are not an animal lover, please remember that all animals are not just dumb creatures. They have feelings if they are hurt, neglected or abused, cold or frightened. Do what you can to help them, be it animal, fish or fowl.

The pet that is loved will give its *ALL* to you in return.

In memory of our darling Tibbs,
who died 1st September, 1995.

Dedicated to all those who love animals and to
those whose lives have been changed by a cat.

PART ONE

NINE LIVES AND ONE MORE

Tibby's Story

CONTENTS

PROLOGUE

This is a story of the life, death and after-life of our beloved cat.

She chose us as her family and lived with us for 12 years. She died at 9.30 a.m. on Friday, 1st September, 1995. After a short struggle for life, she died in my arms. I was talking to her, comforting her, crying, aware of what was happening, praying it would not happen, yet knowing it was best for her. Although I believed she was not in any pain, she was suffering and it was only a matter of time.

An appointment had been made at the vet's for 10.30 a.m. that day and I warned my daughter that Tibbs probably would not come back. She said, 'Goodbye'.

I am so grateful that I was able to be with her in her own home as she died and not have to end her life by other means in the vet's surgery. I know that we did everything we could for her in her life and in her death and she repaid us a thousand times over during her time with us.

GOD BLESS TIBBS ... We miss you and love you.

1

Arrival

I was taken from my mum and sisters when I was a kitten. I went to live in a house where there were a lot of children. I thought my name was 'Cat', because that is what they called me. The man of the house called me, 'that darned cat'. The children cuddled me when I was little and played with me, but as I got older and bigger, they didn't seem to want to play with me. I chased after imaginary pieces of string and balls, but they soon lost interest in me.

The lady fed me when she remembered, but sometimes the bowl with scraps in it was left outside for days and the food got wet and hard. I didn't like it, so I was often hungry. They pushed me out at night. I didn't mind when the weather was warm. The stars twinkled overhead and I could watch out in the dark for a mouse to eat. Soon it began to get cold and it often rained. I had trouble finding somewhere warm and dry to sleep. Now and then I went back to the house, but the door was always shut, and if they saw me they would shout, 'Go away'.

It was then that I heard a new sound in the house. One I had not heard before and did not recognise. There was a lot of crying and screaming. The lady was always talking to the noise. It looked like a small doll. It made a lot of noise – it kicked, it screamed, it demanded a lot of attention and when it cried the lady picked it up and it went to sleep. Of course, no attention was paid to me and I was lucky if I got any food left out for me. I found out later that 'it' was a baby.

The older girls thought I was a dog and although not unkind, they were rough with me. One day they tied a skipping rope around my neck and made me follow like a dog. A kind neighbour told them not to do that. I didn't like it. It made my neck hurt. I ran away and hid for a few days. There were plenty of mice and birds around so I didn't go hungry, but I had to learn to be a bit quicker when hunting for food, because I could only catch baby birds.

I went back to the house after a while, but every time I got near the baby he sneezed and spluttered and cried.

They shouted, 'Get out! *Get out!*' and I got pushed out quite roughly.

I began to think I should have to look for somewhere else to live. I didn't want to stay with that family any more and they didn't want me now they had a baby.

The nights were getting dark and cold, so I decided to have a look around. There must be someone who would like a little cat, who hadn't got a dog or a baby.

2

Moving House

I began to look around at all the other houses and gardens, ones with no babies and no animals. There were a lot of dogs in the neighbourhood and unfriendly cats. A big black cat chased me out of his garden and two puppy dogs ran after me. I saw a lady doing some gardening and I rubbed myself against her leg, but she shouted out at me, waved her arms and threw some water at me.

'Shoo,' she shouted, 'shoo cat, shoo. Off my garden and my flowers. Go home.'

Sadly I ran away. I only wanted to be friendly.

The lady at my old house still left out some scraps now and then on the grass, but they got wet, and often the birds ate them when I was not around. The nights were getting much colder and darker. Some mites were biting me and making my back sore. I had to find a home. Someone *must* want a smart tabby cat.

In the middle of December around 1982 (I'm not very good with dates), I spied a pile of cardboard boxes outside a house. There was a light on in the kitchen, but I couldn't see or hear anyone, especially any babies. I decided to try out the boxes. The top one was quite good. Once inside I was out of the cold and wind. The box smelt a bit funny. It was not a smell I knew, but I was determined to stay. As the night wore on I got used to the smell. In fact I rather liked it. It made me feel warm and cosy, and a bit light-headed. I heard the lady of the house say later that there had been wine bottles in the box. Hmm! that should be on a cat's menu. I slept that night feeling cosy and warm.

I slept in the box for several nights, always making sure I was gone by early morning. The weather got worse, so I started to climb into the box earlier.

One night the lady came out and said, 'There is a cat in the box.'

I jumped out and ran away, but it was cold and wet in the garden and it started to snow. A few days later I crept back and saw that there was a bowl of food near the boxes. Each evening the lady came out and spoke to me very quietly. Every morning there was a bowl of fresh food and some milk and water. After a while I let her stroke me, though I was careful to swear if I felt frightened and then she would go away. She tried to entice me into her kitchen, but I was not having any of that. There might be a baby inside the house or some children.

One night it snowed very hard and the boxes collapsed. The lady was very upset, so the man, her husband, made a wooden box with a roof and an opening so that I could come and go. By now, the bowl of food was getting nearer and nearer to the back door. One particular day it rained very hard and she put my food under a stool so that it would not get wet.

'Well,' I thought, 'she can't be all bad.' Perhaps I could sneak indoors and have a look around when nobody was about.

The next day I looked for my bowl, but it was not there.

'Oh,' I said to myself, 'these humans are all the same – do what they like when it suits them.'

But then I saw it. It was just inside the back door. The door was wide open even though it was very cold. No one was about – or so I thought. I looked around very gingerly, then slowly slunk in over the step, keeping my body close to the ground and my ears pricked for sounds. I gobbled the food down very fast and was just having a quick drink when I spied out of the corner of my eye the lady watching me. She was standing behind the kitchen door, just peeping out. She made no attempt to trap me or speak. I suddenly found myself out in the garden. I don't know how I got there. I had run so fast. The lady came to the back door and was softly calling me.

'Tibbs, Tibbs, come back Tibby,' she whispered.

Tomorrow, I decided, I might go back and have another look. I still had my box. That night the lady spoke to me and stroked me very gently. I answered her with a little miaow.

The next day, there was my food inside the kitchen. The lady was busy cooking, so I sat outside the door and looked at her.

'Come on,' she said, 'come in and eat your food.'

I walked in, still looking around carefully and keeping my ears pricked. I couldn't hear anything except for the soft hum of a radio. I ate my food, not forgetting to say, 'Thank you,' by rubbing up against her leg. Then I went for a walk around. I couldn't see anyone else or hear any crying. I wondered what was upstairs. I walked up cautiously. The lady followed me at a distance.

'Hmm, seems all right,' I said to myself. 'Nice soft beds.'

There seemed to be one or two dark places where I could curl up and hide.

I came inside several days after that for my food and then one night I decided to stay a while. The lady lifted me on to her lap and stroked me, but my back was very sore and she saw it.

'Oh you poor pussy-cat,' she said, 'we shall have to get you put right.'

I was not sure what she meant, but her voice sounded kind, and her hands were soft. I thought I might stay there.

3

The Vet

There were two older children in my new family. They played with me, but they played my games. They would pull a piece of string around for me to jump on. They even bought a toy mouse, but I was not that daft. I knew the difference between a toy one and a real mouse. Still it amused them if I chased after it and tossed it up in the air, until I had had enough. They all laughed and tried to tempt me again, but I would just curl up and go to sleep and they would leave me alone.

The lady was very kind and treated me like a cat. She seemed to understand my nature, but the man, her husband, treated me more like he would a dog. I didn't think he had had much to do with cats. I have heard it said that 'a dog is a man's best friend'. He wanted me to 'sit' and 'stay', and have a 'rough and tumble' with him, but I put out my claws and scratched him, and spat.

'Oh well, that's it,' I thought. 'I expect I will be put outside now.'

The lady picked me up carefully and talked to me. I was still spitting.

'Now then, stop swearing,' she said. 'Calm down and come and sit on my lap.'

She liked to stroke me, but she soon realised that my back was very sore and bleeding and I was scratching a lot. She was very upset. Next day a large cardboard box arrived.

I liked boxes, but once I was in this one I couldn't get out, and I couldn't see anything. I began to panic. I miaowed loudly and scratched the sides of the box. The lady spoke to me, but I just wanted to get out. I could feel movement and hear strange noises. I was in a car. If only I could see what was happening. Suddenly the movement stopped and I was being carried in my box. Doors banged and finally the box was put down on the floor. I was beside myself with fear wondering what was going to happen. I really wanted to do a 'wee', but I couldn't do it there.

I heard a voice, not that of my lady.

'You shouldn't carry a cat in a cardboard box like that,' said the new voice. 'It is very dangerous. The cat can scratch the sides and get out and get lost.'

'Oh dear,' my lady replied.

'Why don't you buy a nice white wire basket,' said the voice more kindly. 'You can buy one here at the vet's, then your cat can see what is going on. It won't be frightened and it will be more secure than a box.'

'Thank you,' said my lady. 'I will do that.'

After that I was picked up in my box and taken into a large bright room. A man in a white coat was there. My lady held me tightly and put me on to a table.

'Well, what have we here,' said the vet. 'This is a scruffy one, to be sure.'

My lady explained how she had acquired me and he said he thought that my condition was due to a bad diet, irregular meals and poor shelter. Though lots of cats are hardy and can live an outdoor life, I was unlucky. He thought that with special care I would improve and be my old self again. Then he stuck a needle in me. It hurt, so I swore and tried to bite him, but he was too quick for me and my teeth sank into my lady's hand instead. I was sorry about that, but she did not scold me. She just stroked me and spoke to me quietly. She put me back into a white wire basket. I could see everything that was going on. I spat at the dogs and swore at the cats on the way out.

For a few weeks my back improved and my fur was soft.

My Mistress, as I thought of her now, stroked me carefully, but my back was still tender. I even climbed on to her lap occasionally, but I spat and hissed if I did not want to be touched. My back became very sore again and bled. My Mistress was very upset, as she had been feeding me properly and doing all the things the vet had told her to do. Suddenly I was in the wire basket again and in the vet's waiting room. There was quite a mixture of other animals there. In one corner there was an enormous dog. I think he was a Great Dane or something like that. All of a sudden a big puddle began to spread from him. Everyone yelled, picked up everything from the floor, including their feet, and me of course. Two girls rushed out with mops and the big dog began to howl. The owner kept apologizing and scolding the dog. The poor thing looked unhappy. His ears went flat, and he tried to crawl under the chair, but he couldn't. He was too big. What a disgrace. I would never do a thing like that, though I did disgrace myself once coming back from the cattery, but you can read about that later on.

Now it was my turn. I was ready for that vet this time. I was going to bite him first and then see if he could stick a needle in me. But again, he was too quick for me and well practised in the art of handling cross animals.

'I am afraid your cat has been bitten by mites,' he said. 'You must spray her every week and we will see how she progresses.'

Spray, what is a spray? I decided to keep clear of the garden hose. These humans think they are clever. They make dogs do tricks and go for walks on a lead, but not me. I made up my mind that if it got too much for me, I would leave and find another home. My Mistress took me home. The big dog was next. I hoped he got a needle stuck into him. He deserved it for making the floor all wet.

4

Sunday Morning

Monday to Friday was always the same. Everyone got up early ready to go to work. The Master got up first and gave me something to eat, then unlocked the back door so that I could go out and stare at the birds. They had been up a long time and they wanted to feed and splash in the bird-bath. My Master had made a beautiful bird table with lots of different things for them to eat. 'Birds on a plate,' I thought, but although I tried jumping up, I couldn't reach them, so I had to lie in wait in the flower beds just underneath. My favourite place was under the holly tree. They couldn't see me, but they knew I was somewhere near. They would fly up into the trees when they saw me come out and make a lot of noise, hoping I would go away.

If my mistress saw me, she would say, 'Leave the birds alone.'

But that is what cats do – chase birds. So I sat under the bird table ready to pounce.

Of course I was not hungry, but something inside me said, 'Catch a bird.'

After a while I got fed up, and asked to be let indoors again. By this time the Mistress's daughter, Sally, was up, so I miaowed loudly and got another bowl of food. I stayed in and watched the birds from a chair in the dining room. It was the chair that Sally sat on.

If she got there first, I would stare at her and stalk round the room until finally she would get up and say, 'All right puss, I know you want this chair. Here you are – I am going to work.'

I would jump up and sit there dreaming of mice and birds. Sometimes I would curl up and have a snooze.

Last of all my Mistress got up. I would rub my head against her leg and miaow softly.

'Oh, you poor starving puss,' she would say, tongue in cheek. 'Hasn't anyone fed you yet?'

She knew full well that I had already had two bowls of food, but I knew how to get round her.

'Never mind, I will give you something to eat.'

So saying, she would pick me up and tickle me behind my ear and then produce another bowl of food. I was not really hungry, but I licked it so as not to upset her. After we had both had our breakfast – in my case, three – my Mistress would sit down in the armchair for ten minutes with her cup of tea and I would climb up on to her lap and settle down for a little nap. Soon it was time for her to get ready for work. My Mistress always told me when she was going out and when she would be back. Most days she came in at lunchtime to say, 'Hello' and feed me. During the winter, she would leave some food down for me at my special feeding place, but in summer she would not, as there were too many flies about and she said if they got on my food it would make me ill.

The house was quiet when everyone was out and I could take my pick of the beds as all the inner doors were left open. In the morning I liked to sleep in the front bedroom on the big bed, because the sun was on that side and it was warm and cosy, also in winter there was a big radiator in that room. In the afternoons I liked to sleep downstairs, so that I could keep one ear alert for sounds of my Mistress coming home.

It was nearly always the same. In the late afternoon, as I snoozed in the armchair, I could hear lots of children's voices as they walked past our house on their way home from school. I would then get up and sit on the window sill.

'Oh look,' some of the children said. 'That cat belongs to our teacher. Isn't she pretty.'

I would purr to myself. I strained my ears and eyes for the first sign of my Mistress. I could hear her feet before I saw her. There she was coming down the street and along the path. She knocked on the window where I was sitting and I jumped down and ran to the front door. She picked me up and talked to me. I purred and answered with a little mew.

She gave me something to eat and then said, 'Let's sit down and have five minutes, Tibbs.'

I liked that part of the day, just me and 'my Mum', as I was beginning to think of her. Afterwards I would go off and find a nice cosy place to sleep till everyone came home and my Mistress would set about her housework.

Saturday and Sunday were different. No one got up early except me and the birds. Nobody was about to give me any food. I made a lot of noise. Once or twice the Mistress left the bedroom door open. I sneaked up at 4.00 a.m. and jumped on the bed and walked carefully all over her and licked her face. She was not very pleased though she did get up and put out some food, but then she went back to bed and shut the door.

Sunday was like Saturday to begin with, but then Sunday changed. It all began when the vet mentioned about a spray every week. The morning started as usual. My Mistress got up, not before time, as I was hungry. I ran up the stairs and scratched carefully at the toilet door. She came out, lifted me up and carried me downstairs. I didn't mind walking down, but it was nice to be carried. She gave me an extra special cuddle. I should have been suspicious when I noticed that the kitchen door was being closed quietly behind me. Before I had a chance to escape I was trapped. What was going to happen?

My Mistress put me down on the floor and ruffled my fur, talking to me whilst holding me firmly, then she sprayed my back. I tried to wriggle away but she had hold of me, at the same time shielding my face.

'All done,' she said.

The kitchen door was opened, so I ran into the dining room and crouched under the table. I started to lick myself, but it tasted horrible.

'There,' said my Mistress following me, 'that will stop the "itsy-bitsys" from biting you.'

What are 'itsy-bitsys'? The taste and the smell of the spray stayed with me all day. I would not go back into the kitchen again.

'All right,' she said, laughing, 'I will put your bowl of food on the other side of the kitchen door.'

I ate it gingerly, keeping a wary eye open for that spray. I ran and hid behind the settee, trying to lick the stuff off my fur. It was not nice. I heard the back door open, so I ran through the kitchen and out into the garden. I stayed out there most of the day. Even rolling on the earth did not get rid of it.

'Watch out for the "itsy-bitsys",' my Mistress called after me.

I'll watch out all right. I'll watch out for that spray, I thought. She won't catch me again.

The week went on as usual, Monday to Friday, and soon I had forgotten all about that nasty spray. That Saturday, as before, they all stayed in bed a little later. I had to make a lot of noise before my Mistress got up. They don't seem to realise, these humans, just what they miss. The birds are all up and singing. Everywhere is a little damp with dew. The sun gets warmer and the spider's web is sparkling with dewdrops. The best part of the day and they spend it in bed. Sunday was the same. My Mistress got up and carried me downstairs. Too late, the kitchen door was closing behind me again. I was not quick enough to escape from that spray.

'It must be Sunday again,' I muttered under my breath. 'I won't get caught next week, or the next, or the next...'

5

Holidays

I never quite got used to that spray, but I suppose it did help. My back got better and my fur was like silk. My Mistress said I was the most beautiful cat she had ever seen.

One morning I was upstairs with my Mum. She was getting ready to go to work when I had a fright. She got out a spray can and began to spray herself. She also had a bottle which smelt quite strong and she sprayed that on herself too. I could not believe my eyes. I was ready to run in case she sprayed me. She even sprayed her hair. Another day I saw the Master spray himself. I wondered if humans had 'itsy-bitsys'? Do they bite their backs and make them sore?

One morning when my Mum was cleaning the bathroom and toilet she sprayed in there. Is that where the 'itsy-bitsys' live? I kept well clear of those two rooms. My Mistress was very brave to go in there with them. I stood guard outside in case she needed help, but just far enough away to run if they came after me.

On one particular day I knew something was going on. There was a lot of talking, and the family were walking around a lot. Some large suitcases appeared and the Mistress was busy putting things in. Later in the day I sneaked upstairs, but all the bedroom doors were shut, so I couldn't hide under a bed. I crept cautiously down the stairs, and stopped in the middle to watch what was going on.

'There you are, Puss,' said Mum, and made a grab at me, but I was too quick.

I ducked under her arm and ran into the dining room and under the table.

'Got you,' growled the Master.

I bit his hand and ran out of the dining room, into the front room and hid behind the settee. They all chased after me. There was my Mum at one end and the Master at the other end: no escape. My Mum picked me up. I was growling and spitting and wriggling, but she had a firm grip on me, just the same as when we were at the vet's, and I was put into the white wire basket. Not that vet again, I thought miserably, but no, the journey was different.

The car stopped, and I was taken out into a sort of office. A jolly man with a soft voice looked at me and asked my Mistress a lot of questions about me. I was put into a much larger cage like a tall box with a wire door. My bed was put at the back and there was a big bowl of sawdust by the door. Later a bowl of food and another with water were also put into the cage.

There were a few moggies like me, but mostly they were pedigree cats. Opposite me was a big Burmese cat. It looked very snooty.

'My people have gone on a cruise,' he said condescendingly.

'Well, mine have gone to Europe,' I replied sharply. I was shaking but trying not to show it. 'And they went on an aeroplane and, what's more, they are coming back on one.'

That shut him up. I didn't know where Europe was or how big an aeroplane might be. I was only repeating what I had heard my Mistress say. Perhaps Europe was down the road and she would be back the next day to collect me. After a while the Burmese and I became quite friendly. He was very 'laid back'. He said he had stayed at the cattery several times.

'Sometimes three times a year.'

One day a small white kitten came in, and that night she began to cry. The other cats told her to 'shut up' and 'stop that noise'. I could see she was very sad.

'What's the matter?' I asked in a friendly sort of voice.

'My Mistress has gone away and left me,' she sobbed. 'She doesn't love me any more.'

'Yes she does love you,' I said.

'Now look here,' interrupted the big Burmese cat in a softer voice than before. 'It's like this. They leave you here for a short time whilst they go on holiday. She will be back, mark my words.'

'Will she really?' asked the little cat, looking a bit more cheerful.

Her name was Fluff.

'Yes,' answered the Burmese, shutting one eye, then the other.

'The trick is,' said a very slender Siamese cat with beautiful black pointed ears, 'not to make too much fuss of them when they come back. Let them see that you are not going to be pushed around. Walk out into the garden before you rub your head against their legs.'

'Of course she will come back,' I said. 'So while you are here make the most of it. You can sleep when you like. You will get your meals on time and you don't have to scratch about in the garden.'

'All right,' said Fluff, 'I will try. Will you be my friend?'

'Certainly I will,' I said trying to sound cheerful, though secretly my heart was breaking too, although I couldn't let Fluff see that.

'Has she gone to sleep yet?' said the Siamese yawning. 'I want to get my beauty sleep.'

At the end of the week, a lady came for the little white cat and really Fluff didn't want to go.

She said, 'Goodbye' and there was a tear in her eye.

'Give 'em hell when you get home,' I whispered.

'Don't talk to them for a few hours,' said the Burmese. 'Make them feel sorry for having left you here.'

But already she was licking her Mistress's face.

Every day, one by one, the cats were let out of their cages into an enclosure whilst their cage was cleaned out. There was a big black tom, who was a bit of an 'Alley Cat', not used to being 'pushed' around.

'I like to be out on the tiles,' he said jauntily. 'Up on the rooftops under the moon, or raiding the dustbins.'

He spoke very defiantly. When it came to his turn to be cleaned out he sat in the corner by the door of the enclosure. He arched his back, growled like a tiger and spat when the girls came to put him back in his cage. We all sat and watched, dumbstruck. The nice man and his wife came and tried to cajole him back with talk of 'titbits', but he would not move. He swore and growled if anyone came near him. The two girls got a broom each and carefully, without hurting him, managed to push him gently back into his cage. He turned his back on everyone and sat at the back of his cage. During the night he scratched up all the newspaper in his cage into small pieces. He said he felt better after that and that he had shown them who was boss, then he gobbled down his breakfast. He never made any fuss again, but I noticed that two brooms were always nearby when he came out of his cage and I think he could see them too, out of the corner of his eye.

By the end of two weeks my Mistress and Master came for me. I was so pleased to see them that on the way home I disgraced myself. The Master was not pleased. As soon as we got home I started to rub my head against my Mistress's leg and purr. She gave me three helpings of food. The cattery was not a bad place. I went there quite a few times. As the Burmese cat would have said, 'Sometimes twice a year'. The owners were very kind to all the cats. The girls who helped often talked to me and stroked me.

6

The Box

When I came home from the cattery it always took me a little time to sort myself out again. I had to make sure things had not been moved in the house, such as my favourite chair or bed. I also had to revisit my secret haunts; the sunny places or the rubbish heap; the shady place under the trees and the bird-watching place under the holly bush. Sometimes I had to reclaim the garden for myself, as the birds had had it all to themselves for two weeks. I let them know that I was back and who was boss. They were a bit annoyed because they had not been fed for two weeks and their bath water had dried up. As soon as my Mistress put out her washing they did the 'dirty' on it.

'I won't feed you if you do that,' she shouted at them.

'Serves them right,' I thought. 'Fancy doing that when someone has been kind.'

The sun shone and I found my favourite quiet place amongst the flowers. The Master suddenly appeared in front of me holding a small black box. He crouched down, then there was a flash right in my eyes. Everything seemed to explode into all sorts of colours. I couldn't see properly. What was he doing? Then another flash. I got up and moved away. He said it was a camera and that he wanted to take my photograph. Who did he think I was – 'Arthur' of television fame? And he's no David Bailey either. When

I saw him getting ready to make the box flash again, I got up and turned my back on him.

A few days later my Mistress had a similar box, but it didn't flash, so I didn't mind. She took several photos of me. I rolled over and did all kinds of tricks. My Mistress kept some fish treats (cat biscuits) in a jar and my best trick was putting my paw in the jar, tipping it over, and hooking out some of the treats.

'Only three,' my Mistress would say, 'otherwise you will be sick.'

I liked them a lot, so if she forgot to screw the lid back on I could help myself. I couldn't count so I didn't stop at three. I ate a lot, but the next day I was off my food and I had to keep eating grass to make me feel better.

One summer a neighbour brought a large wooden box and put it in our garden. There was a funny looking animal inside. It was all white with pink eyes, large floppy ears and a funny little tail. It seemed to like carrots and lettuce. I jumped around trying to make it come out, but it stayed in the corner of the box chewing a carrot. My Mistress brought out her camera box again and took some photographs. She said she would put them all in an album and they would all be of me.

Last year my Mistress and family went out for a day on the Orient Express – very grand. They took lots of photographs, but when they came back there was just one; left on the roll, so she took one of me. When I became ill, my Mum said she didn't want to take any more of me then, because when the time came she wanted to remember me as I was when I was well and full of life.

When something happened to me she said she would have that last one enlarged and framed. I was not sure what she meant, because I was not going anywhere other than the cattery or the vet. They are funny, these humans. They don't always say what they mean.

Summer days were lazy days. I could lie in the sun and snooze. My Mistress was home from school for six long weeks. The only thing I didn't like was going to the cattery, but once I was there I usually saw some of my old friends. The days were longer and the birds were about till late in the evening. The back door was always open and I could come and go as I pleased.

As winter approached I would find a warm place to sleep near a radiator. There was such a place in Sally's room, warm and dark under a shelf. Sometimes she didn't know I was there and in the middle of the night I would creep out, jump on her and cuddle down with her. She never minded and only put me outside the bedroom door when I started to miaow at four o'clock in the morning.

7

Dogs, Cats and Other Animals

Two dogs lived next door to us. I always thought their names were 'shut up', and 'stop barking', but they did have proper names as well. If they caught a glimpse of a cat, they would start making a lot of noise and chase up and down the garden. The neighbourhood cats used to amuse themselves by walking along a high wall between the two gardens and then stop and stare, or wash themselves. The dogs, of course, went mad – barking, yelping and jumping up against the wall. It was then that we heard, 'shut up' and 'stop barking'.

A few houses down the street there lived a black Persian cat. He had a good home but he was a scrounger and would raid the dustbins or tear the black plastic sacks put out for the refuse men, to get at a tasty titbit. He liked to stay out every night and he used to try to persuade me to come out.

On first sight he tried to be the boss, snarling and hissing at me, but if my Mistress saw him she would shoo him away. Gradually he realised that if he lived in peace, we could be friends. Most mornings he used to walk up to the back door, which was shut, and look in.

My Mistress would say, 'Your friend is here.'

I would saunter out into the garden when I felt like it and take up my place above him on an old wooden box. He would creep slowly forwards and sit down, keeping one eye on me and one on my Mistress. As long as he did not appear to want to fight me, my Mistress allowed him to stay. She even put a bowl of milk out for him. When he had drunk it, he would turn and march off, tail in the air. He would jump up and walk along the wall looking at the dogs. Sometimes he would stop and clean himself, oblivious of the noise the dogs were making. Then he would trot off home.

Once he did a bad thing. My Mistress was cleaning out her freezer and she put a large box of frozen meat outside in the garden on a table. The weather was quite cold, so she covered it with newspapers and an old towel. When she went back out to get the meat, the black cat had a frozen chop on the ground and was trying to eat it. My Mistress laughed and laughed.

'Well, if you are that hungry,' she said, 'you can keep it, but you are not having any more of my meat.'

She brought the box in, but just to show him that he shouldn't have done it, she didn't put any milk out for a few days.

The Black Cat, as we called him, was very streetwise and would cross the road despite the amount of traffic that went up and down. My Mistress did not like me to go near the road. She was afraid I would get run over, but I wanted to see what it was like out there. Once or twice I sneaked out when the front door was open. I even managed to get to the Black Cat's house, but my Mistress kept calling and waiting for me, so in the end I went back.

The bottom of our garden was all wild. It was too long for my Mistress and Master to keep tidy, but I loved it. There were all sorts of creatures in the long grass and a lot of mice running about. By creeping under the hedges, I could get into the neighbours' gardens, first making sure there were no dogs or babies around. Some nights in summer I stayed out under the bushes. My Mistress would finally give up calling me and go to bed. Next morning I was always waiting by the back door. After a good feed and a pretend scolding from my Mistress, I usually slept most of the day indoors.

One particular night, when I had decided to stay out, a peculiar thing happened. I was snoozing under the holly bush when a round brown object moved across the grass to some bread on the lawn.

'Too big for a mouse,' I thought, ready to pounce. 'Not as big as a bird - maybe a sparrow out late.'

All the birds were in bed. I moved closer. As I got nearer it saw me and curled up into a ball. I touched it with my paw and got an awful shock. It was much worse than the vet's needle. It was like 100 needles going into me at once. I wailed and retreated quickly to the shelter of the holly bush. The 'thing' uncurled itself and two bright beady eyes stared at me. They seemed to be saying, 'Keep away'. It was a hedgehog. It began to eat the bread, making some funny little snuffling noises, then it moved over to the flower beds. Another larger brown ball appeared and uncurled itself. Behind it were two little ones. I stayed where I was. They didn't seem frightened of me, even though they could see my eyes glowing in the dark.

'Oh well,' I thought, 'if they leave me alone, I will not touch them.'

They came for several nights, but I always kept my distance.

In the spring of my first year with the family, my Mistress had a friend's small Yorkshire terrier for a fortnight. She had looked after the dog before I came. She wondered how the two of us would get on. The dog wanted to be friendly, but I did not. He was almost the same size as me and his name was Pepsi. My Mistress brought him in on a lead to the front room where I was sitting on the window sill. He barked and jumped up at me. I swore and put out my claws.

'Oh dear,' said my Mistress, 'you two are not going to be friends,' and she took the little dog out of the room.

From then on it was separate mealtimes and outings. I was shut in the back room whilst Pepsi had his food in the kitchen, then he was shut in the front room whilst I had my food. I heard my Mistress say that although she loved the little dog, she would not be able to look after him any more as it was not working out very well. He never came again.

Other cats often came into our garden. I think they knew my Mistress was a 'soft touch'. She would sometimes feed them, but if she thought they were going to hurt me, she would shoo them away - after they had eaten, of course.

One winter a large bedraggled marmalade cat kept coming into the garden. He was dirty and kept crying for food at the back door. He didn't seem to have a home. My Mistress was upset at the state he was in, but she didn't want to encourage him in case he had any diseases that he might give to me. After a few nights, my Mistress phoned the 'cat lady' at the Cats Protection League and a lady came for him. She said she knew an old lady who would give him a home. It was quite a business catching him. Although he was familiar with my Mistress, he was a wily old cat. The cat lady put down a wire cage like mine. My Mistress had to catch him and put him in the cage. She put some food down near the cage. He pounced on it hungrily and began to gobble it up. When he had almost finished, she grabbed him, not forgetting to put her gardening gloves on, and put him in the cage. She shut the lid and fastened down the catch. He swore and growled and tried to scratch the caring people through the bars. At least he wouldn't be out in the cold begging for food.

A few years ago my Mistress discovered that there were quite a few foxes around. They came into our garden at night looking for food and water. As they approached the house a bright security light went on. At first they ran away, but after a time they got used to it. They came into the garden and treated it like a playground. The three young cubs would chase after each other, jumping down from low walls and running around, whilst the two adults would look for food and water. They dug holes in the lawn and in the flower beds. They came right up to the back door. Although my Mistress was told that they would not harm a cat, she was worried that they might mistake me for a rabbit. She would not let me out after dark, or early in the morning.

Once when I was sitting under the picnic table in broad daylight a fox came into the garden. He stood still and stared at me. Sally, who was in the kitchen, shouted and clapped her hands and he ran away. I was a bit afraid. My tail fluffed up and when I went indoors I couldn't eat my breakfast.

One day I was in the garden when I saw a mouse flash past me. By this time I was quite good at hunting, so off I went at the 'speed of sound' after him. I knew he was somewhere in the flower beds, so I hunted high and low. He kept very still. I moved away pretending not to look. He thought that was his chance to escape, so he began to creep out of the flowers. I spotted him and the chase was on. Unbeknown to me he climbed up to the top of a fuchsia plant. My Mistress, who was inside the house, could see what was happening and she laughed and laughed. She called the Master to come and watch. The mouse was swaying to and fro on the top stem of the plant, whilst I was running round and round the bush searching for him. I knew he was there somewhere, but I didn't think of looking up. In the end I was so weary that I had to give up, but I was very cross and I wouldn't talk to anyone, not even my Mistress, for some time. When I was safely indoors again, he came down and scuttled back to his mousehole.

'Next time,' I said to myself, 'I will catch him, and eat him all up.'

I went off to find a dark secret place in which to sulk.

My Mistress did not like me catching birds, especially baby ones, though she understood that it was part of my nature. She never scolded me if I caught one, but if she saw me preparing to pounce she would wave the curtains, or clap her hands to frighten the birds away.

'Now then,' she would say, 'leave the birds alone. They haven't done anything to you.'

She never said anything when I was stalking a mouse, although she did scream if one came near her. As she clapped her hands, the birds all flew into the holly bush and started chattering. The noise was deafening. They would sit there until I went indoors, then out they would come as brazen as anything and start to feed or bath in the bird bath. My Mistress liked to watch them, but I had other ideas.

8

My Family

I knew when I chose my family that I would have to 'lick them into shape', so to speak. They had never owned a cat, nor any other animal, as a family. Both my Mistress and Master had been brought up with dogs and rabbits.

The Mistress used to say, before I came along, to the children, 'If you want holidays, then you can't have pets.'

She would not put a dog into kennels as it would fret a lot. When I came she had to rethink her plans. She inspected several catteries before she chose one for me.

'Nice and clean and cosy,' she said, 'and very professionally run. This is the one for Tibbs.'

When it came to holiday time, the cattery was not a bad idea. If Sally did not go with them, she would ask if she could look after me, but my Mum, as she was now, thought I would be better off in the cattery, as Sally would be at work all day and sometimes did not come home until late. I didn't mind because when I came home I got lots of cuddles and fuss. Lots of food and plenty of 'titbits'.

I did not think I would have much trouble training them to cat ways. A head rub or a purr works wonders and climbing on to the Mistress's lap won her over every time. They had to realise that I liked my food in a special place and I only ate what I liked, not always what was put down for me. Also I liked to have special places to sleep, such as the Master's armchair, or Sally's bed, and if those places were occupied, I would glare at the person concerned, or stalk round and round until that person moved. My Mum understood me immediately, but it took some time for the other members of the family to learn, especially the Master.

One day I decided to bring my Mum a present to show her how much I loved her and to say thank you for all that she did for me. A mouse or a baby bird would be nice, but I was not sure she would like that. I hunted around to see what I could find. Whilst walking through the next-door garden I came upon a rubbish dump and on the top was a piece of sausage. I picked it up in my teeth and carefully carried it back to our house. My Mum was in the front room dusting. I put the sausage down in front of her.

She screamed as she thought it was a mouse, but when she realised what it was she said, 'Thank you Tibbs. You have brought me a present.'

She picked me up and gave me a kiss. I was purring for all I was worth.

I think she had it for dinner, as I heard her say to the Master, 'Sausage, beans and chips for dinner tonight.'

When I got very good at catching mice, I caught six and laid them in a row outside the back door. I didn't want my Mum to scream again, so I didn't bring them into the house.

After a while she came out into the garden, and when she saw the mice she said, 'More presents, Tibbs. Thank you.'

She left them outside. I think she had something else for dinner. During the night they all disappeared, so something must have liked them, though I did hear the Master banging the dustbin lid.

If there was one thing in the house that I did not like it was the hoover. It made a lot of noise, and I thought it would gobble me up. My Mum used it a lot. She would put me in the front room whilst she hoovered the back room and stairs, then she put me in the back room whilst she hoovered the front room. I tried to be very brave and stay on the table, but when it got near me I would jump down and run upstairs.

My Mistress's mother used to come to the house sometimes, but she always called me 'He' and although she would not hurt a cat, she didn't really like them. She said they walked all over her flower beds and dug holes and left a horrible smell by her front door. She sprinkled pepper around so that they would stay away.

'Cats have no sense,' she would say, 'not like a dog.'

My Mum just used to smile and look at me.

The other thing I hated was having a tablet. My Mum tried putting it into my food but I knew it was there and I wouldn't eat that bit. Every week she used to grab me, usually when I had just woken up as I was a bit dopey then, and wrap me up in a towel. It was quite a 'to-do' because I would fight to get my claws out and she would wrap me up tight to keep my paws in. I would swear and wriggle. She would talk to me and finally prise my teeth open, whilst the Master popped the tablet on a bit of butter and put it down my throat. My Mum would then clamp my jaws together to make me swallow it. Sometimes I would spit it out and we would have to start all over again. I never won the fight, but it was worth trying. I always got a lot of fuss and cuddles after, but if I got a chance I would take a swipe at the Master with my claws.

It did not take long for my family to become trained in the ways of a cat. I could always get a breakfast from each member of the family provided they did not all come down together. I had only to look at my Mum when she was eating her dinner and she would give me little titbits. When she had finished her meal, I would go round and sit by the Master. It was not so easy to get titbits from him especially if he had rabbit, as he liked it all to himself. Chinese takeaway chicken was very nice too. I think my Mum got left with the rice and noodles.

For most of the time, I could chew and eat anything, but in the last year when I was poorly my Mum used to buy special food and mash or mince it up so that it was easier for me to eat it. I could not eat a large bowlful as I used to, so it was little and often or whenever I asked for something.

The times I loved best were when I climbed up on to my Mum's lap and put my head under her chin and carefully pawed her. I remembered doing that when I was a kitten with my real cat-mum. Sometimes I got a bit carried away and my Mum would gently move my paws, but most of the time she didn't seem to mind. I purred fit to burst and she would gently stroke me. I especially liked having my tummy tickled. After a while I would curl up and settle down on her knee. Somehow I always managed to fit into her lap, though when she got sleepy I would slowly fall through her legs. She would catch me and laugh. I would then move to an armchair or somewhere else just as soft.

Most nights, especially in winter, I would creep upstairs about nine o'clock and have a nice sleep on one of the beds, coming down about ten o'clock for my supper. After that I would slink upstairs again and settle on my Mum's bed, usually on some of her clothes because the smell of her perfume was still on them, and I felt as though I was cuddling up to her. Some time later she would come up to get ready for bed. I tried all the tricks I knew to get her to let me stay on the bed with her. Rolling over on my back, purring, even pretending I was fast asleep, but as she came back from the bathroom she looked at me and I knew I could not stay.

Sometimes I would go back downstairs myself, but other times my Mum would carry me down and settle me in the armchair saying, 'Good night, Tibbs, God Bless. See you in the morning.'

Only if I was not well was I allowed to stay on her bed, but once when the Master went into hospital for five days, I was allowed to stay every night. I wished he would go into hospital more often, but once or twice my Mum got a bit cross when I tried to get her up before the birds, so perhaps it was better for me in my bed and the humans in theirs.

9

The Journey

The journey started for me in September 1994, though at the time I did not realise it. It was the journey through my ninth life. My Mistress believed that one's whole life was a journey, but split up into smaller ones, rather like a train going from Land's End to John O'Groats. You have to change trains several times, and it is your own fault if you miss one of the connections, but with the help of a railway guide there is always another route and you will arrive in the end.

I knew I was not the same as a few years before. I was older and couldn't jump on to the high walls, or run as fast as I used to, but I could still catch a bird or a mouse if I wanted to. That summer my Mum brought me home from the cattery after nearly three weeks. I had been there longer than usual as my Master and Mistress had been on a cruise, a 'retirement present', my Mum said. I knew they would come for me, but it seemed a long time. A few of my old friends were there. Some I saw every year, because if their Mistresses were teachers then we would all be there at the same time. I was very pleased to see my Mum, and I said, 'Goodbye' to all the cats, not realising it was my last visit. On the way back my Mum talked to me a lot. When we arrived home, I went round sniffing everywhere and purring to show them I was glad to be home. Of course a bowl of food was put down for me immediately.

Retirement meant that my Mum was at home all the time. That was nice. I liked her to be around the house, especially as I was beginning to feel unwell. I suddenly found I needed to use the litter tray more, but I couldn't relieve myself. It hurt when I did use the litter, but I kept straining to go. My Mum quickly phoned the vet and off we went. I didn't like going there, but somehow I always felt better when I came back.

'This is cystitis,' said the vet in a solemn voice. 'You must give Tibbs a tablet every day for seven days.'

He also stuck a needle in me, but I didn't really mind because I felt so ill. We went home and I had a long sleep. For a week I had a nasty tablet put down my throat every day. My Mum tried to put it into my food, but I could smell it and I wouldn't eat the food. My Mum had to grab me and the Master put the tablet in my mouth with a bit of butter. It wasn't easy for them, because I put up a fight as much as I was able, but I knew they were only trying to make me better.

After a week I was a lot better, but all of a sudden it started again. The vet said I would have to stay at the surgery for a day, so that they could do some tests. I didn't like that. There was no nice armchair to sleep on and they put a needle in me to take some blood. When my Mum came to collect me, the vet told her I had a kidney complaint and there was not a lot he could do for me. I was about 15 years old, so he reckoned that I had done quite well up to then. My Mum tried all different sorts of food, but I only liked my 'Whiskas' food best. I seemed to sleep a lot more. Having my Mum at home was wonderful.

It became a little difficult for me to digest my food so my Mum fed me little and often. Also I began to drink a lot more water. In December of that year, my Mum went back to work, only part-time, one afternoon and two mornings, so I was not alone for too long. I still had the run of the house and when she was at home I could still do what I wanted. I liked to sleep in dark secret places, but my Mum always looked for me because she liked to know where I was and that I was all right.

In the following spring, I began to feel a lot worse and I was losing quite a lot of weight. My Mum was worried and took me to the vet's again. I was getting used to these visits. I stopped swearing at the dogs, unless they came too close, and I didn't spit at the cats. I sat quietly in my white wire basket and watched what was going on, or listened to the people saying, 'What a beautiful cat.' My Mum was very proud when she heard this, but not more than me. The dogs were always very noisy, barking and yapping. Some of them were scared. I could see them shaking. My Mum always spoke to them, but she kept touching my basket, just to let me know she was there.

'I'm afraid her condition is getting worse,' said the vet softly. 'It will mean a vitamin B tablet every day and an injection once a month.'

I didn't like the sound of that, but I was getting too old to put up too much of a fight at tablet time. I could, however, still swear. The tablets were not very nice and left a nasty taste in my mouth.

A few weeks later, my Mum took me to the vet's for the injection. I am ashamed to say that on the way home I was sick in my basket. The Master was not too pleased because it made a mess on his car seat. I felt sleepy when we got home, so I went and hid under Sally's bed. It was nice and warm and dark under there and she had all sorts of odd things hidden away. For a few weeks I felt a little better, but then when it was time for the next injection I felt poorly again. My Mum took me three times and each time I was sick on the way home. The last time was awful. I couldn't help myself. I was sick and I made a mess on the paper in my basket from my other end as well. My Master said something and opened all the windows. The draught nearly blew me off the seat. He drove fairly fast and said that every traffic light was against him. We seemed to stop and start with a bit of a jolt each time, which made me feel worse. When we got home I was in a terrible smelly state. My Mum wrapped me in a towel and tried to wash some of the mess off me. Cats don't like water. I just wanted to run away and hide, so I scratched and swore and wriggled. At last my Mum had to put me down. I quickly ran upstairs and hid. I tried to lick myself clean. I thought of that big dog in the vet's so long ago, who had made the puddle, and realised how embarrassed he must have felt. My Mum came round with the spray, but she didn't spray me and it smelt quite nice.

A few days later, my Mum rang the vet and said she couldn't bring me to the surgery for the injections any more as I had got in such a state. She explained what had happened and asked if he could come to our house instead. He said he would.

'It will cost you an arm and a leg,' said the Master.

'Not to worry,' replied Mum.

She said she couldn't let me get into that state again and, anyway, the car wouldn't get in a mess any more. In all the vet came five times, but I never saw my Mum without an arm or a leg.

My Mum had not booked a holiday that summer, as she said she couldn't leave me as I was ill and, in any case, the cattery probably wouldn't want the liability of a sick cat. Secretly I was glad, because although the cattery was OK I certainly wouldn't get as much fuss there as I did at home and when I felt ill, I liked to be with my Mum. The vet had told her it was just a matter of time. The summer was hot and I lazed in the shade whenever I could find it. The nights were very hot, as I had to stay indoors, and all the windows were shut. My Mum wouldn't let me go out at night because of the foxes. Also she was afraid I might hide away and not come back. Sometimes during the day if it was hot and she was going out, she would let me stay in the garden. There was a plastic table with a large yellow umbrella, and four plastic chairs, standing in the garden. It was cool under the table, and my Mum always put a cushion on the chair so that I could have a sleep. She never stayed out for very long and she always told me when she was going out and how long she would be.

'I am just going out for a while, Tibbs,' she would say, 'I won't be long. I will be home by lunchtime.'

And she always was.

My Mum stopped giving me the vitamin B tablets, as she thought the taste was putting me off my food. She mashed it all up as I seemed to have difficulty with the lumps. One day she and the Master had steak for dinner. I begged for titbits and managed to eat the pieces all right.

'I don't know, Tibbs,' said my Mum with a laugh, 'you really have got me twisted around your little paw.'

I looked at my paws.

'There I am mashing and mincing all your food,' she continued, 'and you are gobbling down my piece of steak so fast that I hardly have time to eat myself.'

It was the same with the Chinese take-away chicken.

The last week of August, my Master had a week's holiday. On the Saturday I was very poorly, straining to go on the litter, and trying to be sick as well. My Mum rushed me to the vet's.

A new young lady gave me an injection, but she said, 'Your cat is very sick. You will have to decide when the time is right, for her sake.'

She wished us good luck. The injection certainly helped me, but I felt very poorly. My Mum tried to cuddle me, but my poor little body was a bag of bones and it hurt when she picked me up. Sometimes I would catch her having a little cry. Everything was an effort. I sat for long periods in my little basket. It was soft and cosy. My Mum put a bowl of water near the basket, so I could have a drink without having to move too much. I still managed to climb the stairs to my favourite place in Sally's room, so she put a bowl of water up there as well.

On *Monday* I lay around and my Mum said she was afraid to go out and leave me unless someone was in the house. On *Tuesday* the sun was shining, and I wanted to go out into the garden. My Mum opened the back door, but she kept watching to see where I went. She was so afraid I would hide away, as she had heard of a friend's cat who, when it was ill, went away and they never knew what happened to it. I sat in the sun most of the morning. It was warm and soft. The great heat of the summer had gone and it was refreshing to feel a gentle breeze on my back. My Mum kept coming out to see where I was and once she panicked because she couldn't see me under a bush.

I seemed to fall over a lot and I didn't have much energy. I had a drink or a little food and then I just sat crouched down by the bowl. My Mum always picked me up and carried me back to my basket.

Wednesday was the same. I didn't eat or do anything in my litter tray. My Mum had noticed some time before that I had stopped purring and it was becoming difficult to clean myself. I had always prided myself on being spotlessly clean, especially my white front and paws. The Master always said that I was a very clean cat, always licking and washing myself, but my strength had gone. I could just about keep my face clean. My Mum tried not to pick me up too much, because I was so thin. She thought it might hurt me, but she often stroked me when I was in my basket and she talked to me a lot.

Thursday was bad. I felt very ill.

My Mum was crying and I heard her say, 'I don't think Tibbs is in pain, but she is suffering. I can't let her go on like that.'

She phoned the vet's surgery, but my special man was not there till Friday.

'All right,' she said, 'book an appointment for 10.30 a.m. Friday, but if the situation gets any worse, I will have to phone and make other arrangements.'

I didn't really eat anything that day. Even drinking was difficult. On *Thursday* night, my Mum said to the family, 'I am going to sleep downstairs with Tibbs. She may not last through the night.'

So saying, she brought down some pillows and a blanket and slept on the settee. My basket was on the floor just by her feet. Once or twice during the night she came and looked at me and stroked me and I managed a little mew, just to let her know I was still there.

Early *Friday* morning, when the birds started to sing, I got out of my basket and managed to get to the litter tray to do a little wee. I was very wobbly on my feet and I couldn't get back to my basket. I flopped down by the kitchen door. A little later my Mum found me. Very gently she picked me up and laid me on the settee. I managed to purr a little, very softly. My Mum heard me. She talked to me and stroked me. When the Master came down, she said she would like to have a shower and some breakfast. The Master stayed with me and stroked me. A little later, Sally came down ready to go to work.

'You know we are going to the vet's today,' said Mum quietly.

'Yes,' answered Sally.

'Tibbs might not be here when you come home,' whispered Mum.

Sally stroked me and said, 'Goodbye.'

I lay on the settee with my Mum beside me. Around about 9.20 a.m. I started to gasp for breath, and stretched out my paws. I turned over on to my other side. My Mum was holding my head, stroking me and talking to me. Suddenly everything went black. I stopped struggling and gasping. There was no more pain or suffering.

I could not see anything, but I could hear my Mum crying and saying, 'Oh no, oh no.'

She shouted for the Master to come down.

'Tibbs has gone,' she said.

They were both crying. I did not feel sad. I did not feel anything.

'I had better telephone the vet,' she said, 'cancel the appointment and ask them what I have to do.'

I could still hear her talking, but as she spoke, the darkness seemed to get a little lighter and I felt as though I was being carried up very, very gently. My Mum lifted my body into my little white wire basket for its last journey and put my towel over me. The light was getting brighter and brighter. I could still hear everything that was going on in the house.

My Mum was crying and I wished I could rub my head against her leg and tell her, 'It is all right, I'm not ill any more.'

The light was getting brighter and brighter. A brilliant white light, which seemed to be everywhere. I was carried right up into the light. I was completely dazzled by it. I wondered what was going to happen next.

10

The Arrival in Heaven

I seemed to be floating, yet I knew I was moving upwards, right through the light. On the other side of the light, which had now become dimmer, everywhere seemed bathed in sunlight. I found myself walking along a path. It seemed familiar, although I had not been in that place before. In front of me was a mat and it had written on it 'WELCOME'. I looked around; there seemed to be endless gardens and fields. There were three dogs sitting by the mat: two black Scottish terriers and a brown mongrel with floppy ears and a tail that nearly wagged itself off. I stopped and looked at them.

'Hello,' said one of the Scotties, 'we have been waiting for you.'

'I don't know you,' I answered.

I didn't feel afraid of them or want to spit at them.

'No,' they all said, 'but we know your Mistress. We used to belong to her when she was quite small, or at least her mother was our Mistress.'

'Oh,' I said thoughtfully.

I felt a bit unhappy when I thought of my Mistress, because I knew she was sad without me.

'My name is Glen,' said the biggest Scottie, 'and this Scottie is called Penny and that floppy-eared mongrel is called Brandy.'

'Pleased to meet you all,' I said.

'Now,' said Glen excitedly, 'I first met your Mistress when she was three years old. I was a puppy and she used to dress me up in dolls' clothes and wheel me about in her dolls' pram. Everyone said that I was a very good dog. I never snapped or bit her.'

'I came next,' piped in Penny. 'Your Mistress was about eight years old. Sometimes she was naughty and she would kick me a little bit under the table. Her mother couldn't see what was happening, so when I growled Mother would say that I was a naughty dog and put me outside. But your Mistress was sorry afterwards and came and gave me a biscuit.'

'Brandy was not my real name,' said the brown mongrel. 'I belonged to a family and then during the war – you wouldn't remember that Tibbs – my house got bombed and all my family were killed. I ran out into the street and kept running until I found a house with the front door wide open. It was where your Mistress lived with her mother and grandmother. I was very frightened of the air raids, so I ran in through the door. I was shaking all over, and I collapsed in a heap on the mat.

' "Poor thing," said Grandma, "it's ill, give it some brandy."

'Grandma liked a few drops in her tea. They poured some down my throat. When I tried to stand up I fell over, and my four paws spreadeagled out on all sides.

' "It's dead," screamed Grandma.

' "Dead drunk," said Mother, laughing. "You have given him too much brandy." I was out for a few days.'

"How did you all get here?' I asked.

'Well,' said Glen slowly, 'my story is a sad one. You see I was a very good dog and I always walked beside my Mistress without being on a lead. One day they took me shopping. There was a lot of people and traffic about, so when we crossed over a busy road I got lost in amongst all the feet and I began to panic. Foolishly I ran out in the road and didn't see a car coming. A policeman picked me up and took me to the police station. By the time my Mistress arrived I was on my way here.'

'Oh dear,' I said. 'How sad.'

'And me,' said Penny in a chirpy manner, 'I got very ill like you and my Mistress had to take me to the vet's. He stuck a needle in me and I woke up here.'

'What about you Brandy?' I asked. 'Did you become a drunk?'

'No,' said Brandy, 'but those few drops did me a power of good. I lived to a ripe old age.'

Just then a beautiful, sleek, black cat walked up to us.

'Hello,' he said in a very low voice. 'You don't know me, although Glen does. I was the first pet your Mistress ever had. As a matter of fact, I came before your Mistress, so I don't really care for small children. One day your Mum was carrying me around. She was a very little girl and she had hold of me quite tightly. I didn't like being carried, so I tried to jump out of her arms. By mistake I scratched her head. She still has the mark to this day. The Mistress scolded me and told her little girl not to pick me up again. That is when Glen came along. I didn't really like dogs either, but I don't suppose they meant any harm. I have lived here with them for a long time. Sooty is my name.'

'Come on,' said Glen, 'we must show you around.'

The gardens were beautiful, with all sorts of lovely flowers and plants. In the distance I could see trees and fields and what looked like a jungle. I could see lots of big animals – lions and tigers, elephants and giraffes.

'That is where the big animals live,' said Brandy. 'Don't be afraid – they will not harm you.'

'There are two very strict rules here,' said Penny. 'You must not chase after another creature or person and you must not harm anything. If you do, you will be sent away.'

'Who is that person in a brown robe?' I asked.

'That is St Francis,' said Sooty. 'He looks after us with all his cheeky cherubs to help him. Watch out for them, they will tweak your tail or tickle your ear. On their afternoon off they will come and play with you. St Francis keeps an eye on them. He cares for all the animals, big and small. He knows all about you.'

'That lady over there in blue,' said Glen, 'is Mother Mary. She looks after all the children, especially the babies. She will come over and speak to you when she has a moment, but the babies keep her very busy. The golden-haired angels help her. She knows all about you because your Mistress often talks to her. I expect she told Mother Mary what happened to you, and asked her to keep a lookout for you.'

'Does Jesus live here?' I asked, looking around.

'Oh yes,' said Penny. 'You will see Him later. He always comes to speak to new arrivals. He brings His 12 friends with Him, though I have heard it said that Simon Peter and his brother Andrew prefer to go and see the fish. I think they were fishermen.'

'Come now,' said Glen, 'I will show you around the gardens.'

The three dogs and the black cat led me round, showing me all the favourite places. One was a garden where the sun always shone. There were a lot of cats there snoozing. There were shady places and sheltered spots, quiet places under hedges and dark warm secret places to sleep. The sky was blue and little white clouds like puffs of smoke floated by.

'You can always find food and drink when you want it,' said Penny. 'Martha and her helpers in the kitchen see to that.'

'And over here,' said Sooty, softly leading me to a most beautiful garden, 'you can see your Mistress, although she can't see you, and if you are very quiet, you might be able to hear her.'

I was a little sad to think that she couldn't see me, but happy that I could see and hear her. She had stopped crying, except when she thought she saw me on the stairs, or imagined she heard me miaow.

'Will my Mistress ever see me again?' I asked sadly.

'Oh yes,' they all said. 'When she comes up here, she will come and look for you.'

'Of course, some humans don't,' said Sooty haughtily, 'but I am sure she will.'

'Oh well,' snapped Brandy, 'I'm off to find a bone I buried this morning.'

'I will come with you,' said Penny.

'I will stay with you,' said Glen, 'until you find your way around. Do you think you will be happy here?'

'Oh yes,' I said, and yawned. 'I think I will find somewhere to have a sleep.'

I found a lovely spot just like the one in my garden at home. I settled down between the flowers to sleep and dream of mice and birds and my Mum.

I am the Cat who sits in the sun,
till the day is done.
Then wanders home, by the light of the moon.
To sleep the night away.

Goodnight, Tibbs … God Bless.

POSTSCRIPT

May 1996 Easter Sunday

I saw a little tabby cat wandering about the gardens. She looked miserable and hungry. Her fur was matted and dirty and she didn't seem to have a home.

I whispered in her ear, 'You go to number 45. They will look after you there.'

She sat outside the backdoor and miaowed loudly.

I heard the door open and my Mum said, 'Come in little cat. We have been waiting for you.'

PART TWO

THE GHOST OF A CAT

Tabby's Story

CONTENTS

PROLOGUE

After Tibby died, I prayed for another little stray cat to walk into our garden. Every night I looked out of the window on to the street wistfully searching for another homeless cat, but not able to summon up the resolve to go to the Rescue Centre.

About five months later another little stray cat did walk into our lives. I believe quite sincerely that Tibby guided the second cat into our garden and into our hearts. We called her Tabitha (Tabby) and this is her story. She was almost identical in looks to Tibby. They could have come from the same litter if the time span had been different. A tabby cat with similar markings, but a very different nature.

Tibby was 'my cat', but Tabby, who still lives with us, loves everyone in the house. We do not know where she came from or why she left her first home, but we love her very much and I know she loves us.

I will let Tabby tell you her story in her own words.

1

Homeless

When I was a tiny kitten, my brothers and sisters and I were taken to a pet shop. We were put into a pen with a lot of other kittens. There were numerous animals in pens: rabbits, guinea pigs, gerbils, hamsters and puppy dogs. They all made a lot of noise, especially if a human big or small came to see us. The dogs made the loudest noise by whimpering or barking every time something moved. At night most of us went to sleep when it was dark, but the hamsters, who had been asleep all through the day, began to wake up and run round and round the little wheels in their cages.

The owner of the shop shouted, 'Shut up,' or 'Stop that din,' and all the animals cowered down in their pens.

Feeding time, which was twice a day, was always very noisy, as all the animals were hungry, especially us kittens. We missed our mother and her milk. It was not easy to chew the food that was put down for us and as there were so many in one pen, there was never enough food for all of us. One of the kittens, who was bigger than me, used to push and fight to get the largest share. My four brothers and sisters and I stuck together and always managed to get something. One day the big kitten pushed me into a dish of milk. My coat was all wet and sticky, but it tasted good and my sisters helped me to lick my fur. My cat-mum had taught us to be clean and tidy, so we all washed ourselves regularly. We had food, such as it was, and shelter and we were warm and dry, but nobody cuddled us or stroked us or even spoke to us. I remembered how my cat-mum used to lick me and talk to me. Small children sometimes picked one of us up but they were not always very gentle and the naughty ones pulled our tails.

One day a lady came into the shop and looked at us.

She picked each one up in turn and when she picked me up, she said, 'I'll have this one, the one with the sad eyes.'

She put me into a cardboard box and took me home with her. When we got there she lifted me out of the box and sat me on the carpet.

'This is your new home puss,' she announced. 'I don't have a name for you, so I will call you Puss.'

She got a piece of string and played with me. Then she told me all the things I must not do, like scratch the furniture or make a mess. There seemed to be so many rules that I couldn't remember them all. Later that day the man, her husband, came home from work. He was not very pleased to see me.

'Oh,' he said sarcastically, 'I suppose this is going to be your new baby. Well I don't want it in the lounge tearing at the furniture. It can live outside in the shed and have its food out there.'

So that was my new home. It was not too bad and it was dry, though the door was hanging off its hinges. The lady fed me in the morning before she went to work and again when she came home in the evening, but often it was quite late when she returned and I was very hungry. The man next door sometimes gave me some food if I miaowed loudly.

'Poor thing,' he said sadly. 'I don't know why some people have an animal if they can't look after it.'

He was kind, but he had a little dog and it barked at me if I got too close. Once it chased after me, so I stayed out of his garden. Occasionally he put a bowl of food over the fence and took it back when I had finished.

My house was very quiet during the day and all the doors

and windows were shut. Most of the time I stayed in the garden. During the week the man and the lady went to work early in the morning and were not home until late in the evening. Saturday and Sunday they seemed to be around more. I could hear the lady working in the house and singing to herself. Some days the man worked in the garden, but if I got in his way he would give me a kick. Once I rubbed up against his leg, but he threw a handful of earth at me.

'Get away cat, go and catch a mouse,' he shouted. 'Do something useful to earn your keep.'

When the man went out in his car, the lady came out into the garden and talked to me. One time she left the back door open and I crept in over the step into the kitchen, but at that moment the man came back.

'OUT,' he yelled. 'Sandra, I told you not to let that animal in here,' and he chased me out into the garden.

The lady looked through the window at me, but the man slammed the back door with a bang. In winter the shed was not very good as the door was almost off its hinges and when it was windy it banged to and fro. The cold wind came through the cracks and the rain dripped through the roof. I had a job to find a dry corner to sleep in. Sometimes the man and the lady were away all weekend. She put some food and water in the shed, but after that was gone I had to fend for myself. I soon learned to catch a bird or a small mouse.

One particular day I noticed a lot of activity in the house and some large wooden boxes appeared. Old shelves and other items were thrown out into the garden. There was also a lot of noise and several people seemed to be walking about in the house. I thought I should make myself scarce as they did not seem to be in the mood to talk to me. I stayed at the bottom of the garden until quite late in the evening. It was spring time, so the evenings stayed light for a long time. When I became hungry I thought it must be time to go home. The back door was shut and there were no sounds coming from the house. I waited and waited, but no one came. Eventually I fell asleep. I woke up early the next morning feeling very hungry. I miaowed loudly at the back door, but no one appeared. I waited for a long time but there was no sight or sound of anyone. I went off to hunt for something to eat. I came back to the house several times that day, but it was always the same. There was nobody about and it looked empty, so I spent a miserable night in my shed. My tummy rumbled with hunger, and the rain dripped on me. All I could do was lick my wet fur.

I went backwards and forwards to the house for many days until eventually I came back and even my shed had been pulled down. The back door was open and there was a lot of noise and banging inside the house. Two people were talking and shouting and some children were running in and out of the kitchen. When they saw me they chased after me.

'Puss, Puss,' they shouted. 'Come here, pussy cat.'

A little boy grabbed hold of me very tightly and carried me into the house. The other children laughed and shouted and tried to pull me away from him, but he held on to me. He was hurting, me so I miaowed and jumped free. A lady, one I did not know, came to the door and hollered.

'Don't play with that mangy cat, it might have fleas. Shoo cat, shoo. I'll set the dog on you. We don't want you here.'

She turned to the man and said. 'The other people who sold us the house must have left the cat behind. We don't want it. I have got enough to do with the children. I don't want another mouth to feed.'

I slunk away to the bottom of the garden. It was no good going next door, I could hear the dog barking. It was time for me to look for another home.

2

Finding a New Home

I wandered around the gardens. There were plenty of trees and bushes, so there was always somewhere to sleep. The weather was not too bad. I hoped I could find a home before winter, as I did not fancy sleeping out in the snow. One garden I visited had a picnic table and chairs covered by a big plastic sheet near the back door, so I could hide under there and watch for birds. There was a bird table in the garden with all sorts of food on it, so there were always plenty of birds around. They made an awful noise chattering and fighting over the food. There was enough for all of them, but the starlings chased the sparrows away. There was also a large bird bath but the larger birds took possession of that and splashed about making a terrible mess on the patio.

'What silly birds,' I thought. 'Fancy making themselves all wet like that.'

I stayed well away when they were bathing. I hid under the table watching for a small sparrow to come my way. I didn't really like eating birds, but sometimes there was nothing else. Another garden nearby was very overgrown and had a tumbledown shed standing at the bottom. The door was wedged open, so sometimes I slept inside it, but there was a family of foxes that also lived in the garden and they thought the shed belonged to them. They snarled at me, but I stood my ground and hissed at them. I arched my back to make me look bigger, my ears flattened and my tail bristled up. They kept their distance sensing an attack, aware that my claws were very sharp. Although I put on a brave show I was quaking inside and I was very scared that they might lash out at me. I didn't go into the shed unless the weather was really bad.

Often I went back to the 'friendly garden' as I began to think of it. It was strange, but whenever I went there I seemed to feel a 'presence'. I couldn't understand what it was, but I felt as though there was another cat there, though I did not see one. It felt friendly and I was not alarmed by it. Most cats are very territorial and when another cat invades their space they fight and become very aggressive, but I did not feel that and the other cat never showed itself to lay claim to the garden. It was as though it was quite content for me to be there, therefore until such time as the other cat chased me away I decided to stay. Once or twice when the moon was full, I thought I saw a tabby cat. It had a grey light surrounding it and seemed to glide noiselessly from bush to bush. It didn't appear to look at me, rather through me. It seemed friendly so I moved a little closer, but as I looked it disappeared like a puff of smoke. I looked into the house and saw a man and a lady. However, I hid under a bush in case they saw me and shouted at me. If the other cat lived there, they would not want me. The foxes were getting bigger and stronger and I was afraid of them, so I decided to find somewhere else to sleep.

One morning when I was hiding in the bushes in my 'friendly garden' the man came out and opened the big doors of his garage.

'Well,' I thought, 'if it is home for a car, then it must be all right for me.'

When the man drove his car out of the garage, I crept in. It was a lot bigger than the shed at my old home and there were a lot of odd things in it. It looked like a junk shop.

'Perhaps cars like it that way,' I said to myself.

Then I heard the man coming back and he started to shut the doors so I hid behind some planks of wood. The doors were shut with a bang and I heard the sound of keys being jangled. I was very scared by all the noise, but it was warm and dry and away from the foxes. I wanted to do a 'wee' but there was no earth to dig, so in desperation I had to do it on the cement floor and I couldn't cover it up. Cats like to cover up their mess so that other animals do not know they are around, unlike foxes who leave it uncovered. My cat-mum had told me 'Always be a clean cat, wash your face and cover your mess.' I looked around me at all the unfamiliar things on the walls, up in the roof and on the shelves. Cats are very curious creatures, so I began to explore. The shelves were lined with old tins and boxes. Above me in the roof were all sorts of odd things. I thought I could probably find somewhere up there to hide and keep warm and safe, then when no one was about I could climb down and look for food. I climbed tentatively up some pieces of wood and up into the rafters. There were ladders, buckets, a watering can with a hole in the bottom, some wood and wire, everything you could think of. I sniffed and pawed them. They did not seem suitable to sleep on, but there was a dark corner, so I got down on my haunches and began to doze.

Much later I was awakened by more noise. The bolts of the garage doors were pulled back and the doors swung open. I heard the sound of a car engine. It stopped and the car door slammed. Suddenly I heard a man's voice.

'Have you had the doors open?' he inquired of the lady.

'No,' she replied somewhat bewildered by the question. 'Why?'

'There is some mess here on the floor,' he answered. 'Surely the foxes haven't been in here and it is not mouse dirts.'

'I haven't had the doors open at all,' responded the lady rather indignantly. 'It looks like cat's mess to me,' and she peered discreetly at the offending mess, 'but I haven't seen any cats around, not even that little tabby who was in the garden the other day.'

The man shut the doors and went into the house, leaving the car on the driveway. When they had gone I thought about trying to get down, but it seemed a long way down from the roof. I was rather frightened and my legs felt wobbly. I retreated into the corner. Perhaps I would try again later. Some time later one door opened and the lady came in.

'Puss, puss, where are you?' she called quietly. 'Come on puss, come down, I have got some food for you.'

I could smell the food but I was too afraid to move. I could hear her walking round and round looking for me. Eventually she put the bowl down and went out, leaving the door open. I tried to climb down but I couldn't. I didn't feel safe walking on the planks of wood. When it got dark the lady came back with a torch.

'Puss where are you?' she said in a soft voice, and shone the torch up into the roof. 'Oh, there you are,' she whispered excitedly. 'Come down and have something to eat.' She called to the man. 'There *is* a cat up in the roof. Perhaps, if you put the car in the garage it will jump down on to it. I will leave the bowl of food and some milk, and maybe that will encourage it to come down.'

He drove the car in, but it made a lot of noise and there was a funny smell, so I decided I was better off to stay in my corner. After a while the doors were shut and locked. It was dark in the garage. I was hungry, but I shut my eyes and went to sleep. Perhaps tomorrow I could get down.

3

The Rescue

It was not too bad up in the roof. At least I was away from the foxes and it was warm and sheltered from the weather, though it was very dark at night. I couldn't see the moon or the stars.

The next day, after the man had gone to work, the lady kept coming into the garage. She brought in some steps and climbed up to try to find me, but I managed to stay well hidden. She brought food and milk and left it on the concrete floor. I was a bit unsteady walking round on the planks of wood as some of them moved slightly when I stepped on them. Mostly, I stayed in the corner, but I was getting very hungry and thirsty. That evening the man got a ladder and a torch and started to call to me. I miaowed once or twice because I thought he was trying to help me, but every time he got near to me, I ran to the other side. He began to get a bit cross and said some bad words, so I didn't think he was very pleased with me.

The lady sounded worried and I heard her say, 'If we can't get that cat down soon, we shall have to phone the RSPCA.'

All evening they tried to reach me, but I was too quick for them.

The man got cross and said, 'I am not wasting any more time. The cat will come down when it is hungry.'

And with that he drove the car in for the night and shut

the doors. I was hungry and I would have got down if I could, but I was afraid. It was easy climbing up, but it looked a long way down and I was shaking with fright. The long night passed. There was no one to talk to, not even the foxes, but I could hear them running about in the garden. In the early morning I heard the birds chattering away.

Again the man went to work and the lady came in several times during the day.

Then in the evening I heard the man say, 'By hook or by crook, we are going to get that cat down, otherwise it will be a dead cat.'

I didn't much like the sound of that. He put the ladders at one end of the garage, and a pair of steps at the other end. The lady climbed onto the steps.

'I can see it in the corner,' she exclaimed timorously to the man. 'I can see its eyes glinting in the dark.'

Bit by bit they barricaded the different paths that I could use until I was almost cornered. I decided to make a dash down to the other end of the roof, but halfway I had to stop to see which way to go as the man had put buckets and wire to stop me. Just as I was trying to work out a route, a pair of hands grabbed me.

'I've got the cat,' yelled the lady excitedly, 'but I can't get down with it as my arms are through the rungs of a ladder.'

'Hold on,' shouted back the man. 'I'll come up there with the ladder.'

I tried to get free, but I really was relieved that someone was trying to help me. The man grabbed me with gloved hands.

'Got yer,' he said, smiling, and climbed swiftly down the ladder, holding on to me tightly.

By now I had got my second wind and I began to struggle and kick.

'Quick, open the door,' he shouted, 'before it goes back up again.

The door opened, and I shot out like a rocket going to the moon. Up and over the fence and back to my shed. The man and the lady stood and roared with laughter.

'I have never seen anything move so quickly,' said the lady shaking with laughter. 'We thought the cat would be half-dead and there it is moving at the speed of light.'

'Faster than that,' retorted the man doubled up with laughing. 'It reminded me of a "Tom & Jerry" cartoon, when the dog chases after Tom. I don't think we shall see *that* cat again.'

'What a pity,' sighed the lady.

I went back to my shed and sat and quivered. I was too frightened to even think about the foxes, food or water. I curled up and went to sleep. The foxes were out hunting and when they came back they took no notice of me.

The next day, when I had calmed down, I decided to go back and try the 'friendly garden' again. The lady had sounded kind and it was funny, I couldn't explain it, but there seemed to be something different about that particular garden. I got the feeling that there was something there looking out for me. Whatever it was I was not afraid and I felt I was not alone there. I looked for another cat or dog, but I couldn't see one, although I thought I heard a miaow. Perhaps I was dreaming. I sat under the picnic table and waited. By this time I was very, very hungry, so I miaowed to let them know that I was there. The back door opened and I heard the lady say, 'I thought I heard a cat crying.'

She lifted up the cover over the table and suddenly I became very scared and ran as fast as I could down the path.

'It's that cat,' she exclaimed. 'It does look a bit scruffy. I don't think it has got a home.'

I stayed at the bottom of the garden where it was overgrown. The lady couldn't see me. Just then I got that feeling again, that there was a friendly being around.

I couldn't see anything, but I could swear I heard it say: 'Go on little cat, the lady will feed you and look after you and give you a home. Go down the garden and miaow.'

I went forward out of my hiding place and sat on the path some distance from the house. The lady walked very slowly towards me holding out a bowlful of food. She spoke quietly to me.

'Come on little cat,' she said quietly, 'here is some food for you.'

She put it down quite near to me and walked slowly backwards to the back door. When I realised it was safe I pounced on the food and ate it ravenously and then ran away.

'That's better,' I said to myself. 'I wouldn't mind some more of that.'

Towards evening I sat on the path again and the lady came out with more food, but this time she didn't come right up to where I was. She stopped halfway along the path and put the bowl down.

'Come on little cat,' she whispered softly, 'come and get your food.'

I got up and walked cautiously towards her. I was hungry but I did not want to be trapped or hurt. I licked the bowl clean and then I sat for a little while. The lady talked to me softly. She sounded nice and kind, but I went back to my shed to think what to do.

The next day, Sunday, she was out in the garden calling me. I crept over the fence and walked slowly along the garden path. This time the bowl was nearer to the open back door. I ate the food, a bit slower this time and licked my mouth and cleaned my whiskers.

'Would you like some more,' she said and brought out another bowlful. Then she went inside the house leaving the door wide open, so I thought I would sneak in and have a look around.

'If there is another dog or cat in there,' I muttered to myself, 'then I will be out of there pretty quick.'

There were some people talking and laughing in the front room.

'Hello, come for a look round?' one of them asked.

I just looked at them and ran out into the kitchen to make sure the back door was still open so that I could escape if I wanted to. After a while I went back into the house again and slipped unnoticed upstairs.

'Hmm. Looks all right,' I murmured. 'No animals, just comfortable-looking beds and hidey-holes. I think I would like to stay.'

I stretched out in a corner of the bedroom. After all that food I felt sleepy.

'The foxes can keep the shed,' I said to myself. 'I think I have found the home of my dreams.'

Then I shut my eyes and drifted off to sleep, to dream of things that might be.

4

The Vet

I was still very frightened by any loud or unexpected noises. The lady realised that, so when she gave me my food in the kitchen it had to be very quiet with no one walking about near me, otherwise I cringed, ran and hid myself. I also liked the back door open so that I could escape if I wanted to.

'Good job it is summer time, little cat,' murmured the lady. 'We shall have to find a name for you. I think Tabitha sounds nice, then I can call you Tabby. My other cat was called Tibby, so now I have Tibby and Tabby.'

She told me all about Tibby. How she had been a stray just like me but had come in and lived with the lady and her husband and how she had loved Tibby very much and missed her now that she had died.

'I wonder if Tibby sent you,' she said thoughtfully.

I began to wonder if that was the cat that I could sense in the garden, but the lady said Tibby was dead, so how could that be? I liked my new home a lot and the lady and the man talked to me and stroked me. The man didn't like the name Tabitha very much, but as he couldn't think of anything else, I became Tabitha (Tabby), with a new home and family.

I spent my days exploring my new house, but I did not go very far away. I always stayed in the garden because I was afraid that if I did go off, I might get lost and not be able to find my way back. The lady too seemed worried that I might get lost, so she bought me a beautiful blue collar. It had a small bell attached to it, but she took the bell off.

'You don't want that tinkling noise right under your nose, Tabby, do you?' she said.

Instead she got a little tag with my new name and address on it.

'Now if you should get lost, someone will know where you live.'

So saying, she put the collar around my neck, checking to see that it was not too tight. I liked my new collar. I had never had one before. I felt very proud, so I purred as loudly as I could.

'You are such a good puss,' the lady said, patting my head, 'You have not made any fuss about the collar.'

When her husband came home he looked at me and declared, 'What a smart looking cat, Tabby. Now you won't get lost.'

None of the other animals have got a posh collar like me. I'll show those birds a thing or two in the morning.

My fur was very matted and my paws were a dirty grey instead of white. My new lady spent a lot of time brushing my coat very carefully to get out the matted fur. She did not hurt me and in fact I quite liked being brushed, but I was not so keen on being combed. The comb tugged and pulled my skin even though the lady was very gentle. I wriggled a lot when she combed me, but I stayed very still and purred when she brushed me. I think she got the message. All the time she spoke to me quietly.

'You are a beautiful cat,' she said over and over.

Her voice was soft and she really meant it. The man also spoke to me a lot and stroked me, but he often stroked me when I was washing myself and most cats like to attend to their ablutions undisturbed. However, he meant well.

Most of the time I rolled over and he tickled my tum. If I wanted attention, and it was not hard to get, I just rolled over with my front paws tucked under my chin and blinked at them. Then they would both laugh and sit on the carpet and play with me.

The lady got up at 6 o'clock every morning to feed me while her husband, the man, was in the shower and getting ready to go to work. It was very quiet in the kitchen and after a while I could eat with the back door shut and not worry about the need to escape. After I had eaten, the lady played with me. She had a pretend mouse on a piece of string. I liked the game and pounced on it as if to make believe it was a real mouse. But I soon got tired of playing. The mornings were getting lighter and I liked to sit at the downstairs window and watch the birds. When the man came down, the lady had her shower and then had her breakfast. She did not mind opening the back door then.

As she said, 'I can see what she is up to.'

She was afraid I might bring a mouse or bird into the house and although she understood why cats hunt birds and mice, she didn't want one, alive or dead, indoors. Her other cat, Tibby, used to bring dead mice in as presents and once brought in a piece of sausage.

After a few months, when I had settled down, the lady thought it was time she took me to the vet's to have some injections against cat diseases. A white wire cage appeared. I sniffed it, but it smelt friendly, though I wondered what it was for. The lady lifted me up and put me in the basket and shut the lid. I was frightened so I miaowed loudly.

'It's all right, little cat, we won't be long,' she promised. 'We are just going for a short ride in the car.'

She wondered if I would travel happily in the car after my experience in the garage. The basket, with me in it, was put on the back seat of the car and the lady sat next to me and talked gently to me all the time. I settled down after a while as it didn't seem too bad. The car stopped and she lifted the wire basket out of the car. It was rather windy and the basket swung about from side to side, so I began to miaow again.

As the lady walked along carrying me she declared, 'My, my puss, you are a heavy cat.'

We arrived at the surgery and could hear a lot of noise. There were cats miaowing and dogs barking. The dogs sniffed the cats' baskets, and the cats spat back at the dogs. My lady sat down and put the basket on the floor. Next to us was a girl with two kittens in a plastic basket. They were mewing and pushing each other to get to the front of the basket. My lady spoke to them and told them how pretty they were. I thought they were very noisy. I settled down in my basket to watch what was going on. A man came in with a very big dog. Someone said it was a Dobermann, but the poor thing was shaking from head to toe.

'We only come 'ere once er year,' he said in a gruff voice, 'but as soon as we gets to that there door, 'ee begins ter shake. 'Ee looks like er bully, but 'ees a big pushover, arn't yer Olly.'

Everyone laughed and the dog started to whine and whimper. If I could speak dog language, I would have told him to 'be quiet,' but he was a lot bigger than me. The door of the vet's surgery opened and a lady with a small dog came out. The dog was called Pansy. What a name for a dog! I wouldn't be seen dead with a name like that. It was so pleased to be coming out that it leapt around on its lead barking and creating such a fuss that I couldn't hear myself think. It backed into my basket and knocked me off my feet. I spat at it. Silly creature. Cats don't behave like that.

'Now, now,' reprimanded my lady. 'It's all right, I am here.'

Our name was called next and my lady took me in and told the vet how she had found me, or rather how I had chosen to live with her, and her family. I sat very still on the table. To tell the truth I was too frightened to move.

'I don't know her age,' my lady explained, 'and I don't know where she has come from.'

The vet looked in my ears and mouth and all over me. He was kind but firm.

'Well,' he said looking at me thoughtfully, 'I would say she is about two and a half years old. She is a bit on the fat side, have you been feeding her up?' He prodded me and laughed. 'But she is not pregnant. I will give her the first injection today, then bring her back in three weeks.'

'What a cheek,' I thought, 'fancy talking about me like that.'

I felt a slight prick, but it did not really hurt me. I don't know why those other animals made all that fuss. Then I was put back in my basket and we went home. Well, that wasn't too bad. In fact I quite enjoyed the car ride. When we got home my lady gave me a big bowl of Whiskas.

A few weeks later the wire basket appeared again.

'Oh dear,' I thought, 'this spells trouble. I think I will creep upstairs and keep out of the way,' but before I had a chance to move the lady grabbed me and put me into the basket and on to the back seat of the car again.

There were not so many animals in the vet's waiting room this time, at least not ones that I could spit at. A boy had a gerbil in a cage and a lady had two baby rabbits in a large box. Soon it was our turn and I was lifted up and put on a big table. A large pair of hands started to prod me and three pairs of eyes looked down on me. All of a sudden one of the people stuck a needle in me; but it didn't hurt.

'Well, she seems all right,' said a man in a white coat assertively, 'but she is much too fat. I think you should cut her food down a bit.'

Hmm. I didn't like the sound of that, but not to worry, cats have a way of getting round their owners if they want to. Too fat, indeed. My lady says I am cuddly.

'She only has a small tin of Whiskas and a small piece of fish or a little tin of tuna,' answered my lady rather indignantly.

'Too much,' exclaimed the man in the white coat. 'Fat cats, like fat humans, are prone to heart disease. Do you know that if you fed your cat on water and vitamins only, I am not suggesting that you do, that it could survive for six weeks?'

'Did you hear that,' I muttered to myself just as indignantly as my lady, 'Water - vitamins, no thank you. If my lady does that then I am off, but I don't think she will.'

'She has got a bit of conjunctivitis in both eyes,' uttered one of the other persons, a student I think as she seemed more nervous than me.

'I will give you some drops,' said the man in the white coat, obviously pleased with her diagnosis.

My lady put me back in the wire basket and off we went. When we got home she opened the lid, picked me up and gave me a cuddle.

'Water and vitamins,' she said with a scoff. 'Not for you, puss.'

I must say I was very pleased to hear her say that. Later that evening she wrapped me up in a towel and held my head still while the man put some drops in my eyes. My sight went all misty for a time, but then it cleared. My lady stroked me and talked to me, telling me what a good puss I was. My eyes had been itchy for some time and I had not been able to clean them properly, so perhaps they were trying to help me.

For several days after they did the same thing. I began to get wise to it and ran and hid, but the lady was quite clever with cats, and she knew how to pounce at the right moment. I reckon she would be good at catching mice - better than me because I keep losing them. Yesterday I had one in my mouth and twice it got away from me and eventually disappeared into the flower beds. Maybe the vet was right, perhaps I am too fat. Anyway, as I was saying, the lady held on to me while the man put a few drops into my eyes. They felt a lot better, and not so itchy. I was sure I could see better. Watch out mouse, I'll get you next time. As the days became warmer I liked to disappear after breakfast and not come back until evening, just in time for my tea. Sometimes it was fish or tuna. The lady and the man had boring old chops or steak and kidney pie. I ate my food quickly in case they preferred mine to theirs. You never know with humans.

5

Adventures in the Dark

One evening after I had finished my tea, the lady said I could go out for half an hour, as I had been in all day, while she had been at work. What is half an hour? I can't tell the time – is it half a day, half a dish of Whiskas, half the night. I had no idea, so out I went.

I have decided to call the lady, Marnie. I don't know why I chose that name. Perhaps it sounded a bit like Mummy, but she is not my mum. She doesn't lick me like my cat-mum used to, but she does kiss me and I know she loves me, so I have decided that Marnie suits her.

I haven't thought of a name for the man, because I can't remember my cat-dad, though my cat-mum used to say, 'He was a handsome black cat, very sleek and wordly-wise.'

I don't know what happened to him. Perhaps he didn't want to be bothered with a litter of noisy kittens. No doubt he preferred to be up on the rooftops on a moonlit night under the twinkling stars. My cat-mum certainly got stars in her eyes when she talked about him and she would never have a bad word said about him.

'Oh well, who needs him?' I said to myself. 'I can look after me.'

But I did sometimes think about him, especially when the moon was bright.

To get back to the evening in question, Marnie said I could go out for half an hour. She was worried about letting me out sometimes. I couldn't always go out just when I wanted to, especially when it was dark. She would not have a cat flap in case all the cats in the neighbourhood used it. That happened to a friend of hers. When the friend came home there were six unknown cats sitting on the mat waiting to be fed. Another friend, called Jean, also had a cat flap and the cat had a magnetic collar, but it had been rooting round the tool shed and had got lots of nails and screws magnetised to its collar, so that it could not get in through the flap. What with the wailing of the cat and the jangle of the hardwear, the whole street was woken up and looked out of their windows to see where the murder had been committed. After that Jean called the cat Beau Jangles.

'Besides, puss, I like to know where you are,' said Marnie.

So out I went. I ran down the path to my favourite places – the rose garden, the holly bush and a mound of stones. The bottom half of the garden was wonderful because it was all overgrown. The whole garden was too big for Marnie and the man to look after, so the front half was kept neat and tidy, but the back part had been left to go wild. There was lots of long grass and piles of garden rubbish, with overgrown hedges to hide under and old pots and bricks to sniff. The foxes often came into the wild part of the garden and they brought all sorts of toys and items they had taken from other gardens. There was an old shoe, a tatty garden glove, squeaky toys, a ragged Sindy doll and an old teddy bear with an arm and a leg missing.

'I should have a lost property morning,' remarked Marnie to her husband. 'These things must belong to someone. We have enough rubbish of our own without having all the neighbours' things as well.'

I loved to sniff about for a mouse, or just sit and watch for one to come scurrying by. I found a place under the hedge and I sat and waited. It was dark under there, but I could see better in the dark and my eyes glowed like emeralds. I shut them so it looked as if I was asleep, but I could still see through the slits, enough to see if a mouse or a small creature ventured past my hiding place. Cats can stay very still for hours if they want to. I could hear Marnie calling me, but I stayed very still and quiet. I did not want to go in. I had only been out a little while and she had said half an hour. Well, whatever that was it was not time to go in yet. She called and called for some time, then she went back into the house.

'This is fun,' I thought, 'I like it out here.'

I couldn't hear any birds chattering as they had all gone to sleep. They are silly things. They wake me up early in the morning with all their noise. They feed and chatter all day long and then when it gets dark, the best time of the day, they all go off to bed.

'What was that?'

I heard a noise. Something was moving about. It might be a fox, so I kept very still as I remembered them from my days of living rough. They wouldn't hurt me unless they thought I was a rabbit, but they were very curious. If they came too near I could puff myself up and bristle my tail and snarl at them, then they would know it was me and go away. They knew I could hurt them with my claws, so they usually went off in search of some other prey. I didn't mind them, especially the cubs, but Marnie said they dug holes in her garden and left their 'dirts' outside the back door.

'They are all God's creatures,' she said lovingly, 'but some are more likeable that others. Like you, puss.'

Often, when I wanted to go out after supper, she said, 'No Tabby, you can't go out. It is dark and the foxes are about.'

But here I was out in the dark. Marnie was calling me again and the man was walking about with a torch.

'Tabby,' they called, 'Tabby, where are you? Come on, come in and have some biscuits.'

Marnie rattled the biscuit tin. Oh no, I was not falling for that one. I was not hungry, well not much, and if I went in for some biscuits, they would shut the door and that would be me in for the night. It was much more fun outside in the dark. The stars twinkled overhead and the moon shone brightly. It was a beautiful night. It is a pity humans don't stay out more at night. It seems to me it is much more fun than going out in the daytime. Animals could teach humans a thing or two.

I had been out a long time and I hadn't seen a mouse. I was getting a bit hungry and I needed to stretch. Just then I heard a strange noise, like another cat, but I couldn't see one. Then I heard a cat-like voice.

'Tabby, go home, your Mistress is worried about you. She is waiting by the door. Tabby, go home.'

'Who's there?' I whispered, startled by the sound. 'How do you know my name?'

Then I saw the 'grey cat'. I saw her sitting a little way away on the path. A tabby cat sitting in the moonlight. She looked ethereal – ghost-like. She started to walk towards me.

'Go home, Tabby,' she breathed.

I stayed very still and looked at her. Was this the 'presence' I felt in the garden, the cat I thought was there but couldn't see? Tibby, the beloved pet of the lady? Tibby, who had died? How could this be? Some animals have a sixth sense, so I had heard. Was this mine?

'Come along, Tabby, I haven't got all night. Your Mistress is very kind to you, and you are making her worry that you might get lost. The Master is worried also. They both love you and you have had your fun. Time to go home.'

'All right,' I said.

Secretly I was glad to go as it was getting rather damp and I was hungry. I followed her down the garden towards the house. The lights were on and I could see Marnie sitting in the window looking for me.

'Goodbye,' said the "grey cat". 'Be good now and go straight in. Rub yourself against your mum's leg to tell her you are sorry.'

The back door was open just enough for me to squeeze through. I looked around, but the "grey cat" had disappeared. Marnie waited until I was right in, then she shut the back door quickly and picked me up.

'You are a buggy-bug.'

That was her way of telling me off. I suddenly realised that I was very hungry. I struggled to be put down, then I rubbed myself against her legs and purred. That is my way of saying, 'Sorry, but I am very hungry, where's my food?' Marnie put a bowl of Whiskas down in my special place and in no time it was all gone.

'That was quick,' exclaimed the man.

'Miaow,' I said, 'can I have some more, please?'

'You shouldn't have stayed out so long,' replied Marnie, refilling my dish.

Whoosh, that was gone as well. In no time at all I was running up the stairs to my bed.

'Well I never,' said Marnie to her husband, laughing. 'Here we are worrying ourselves in case Tabby gets lost and now she is upstairs with a tummy full of food and curled up in a little ball far away in dreamland. Perhaps we can go to bed now. Goodnight, little cat, sleep well.'

'Goodnight,' I murmured in my dreams. 'Goodnight, grey cat.'

Was it the Ghost of Tibby?

6

The Grey Cat's Story

My name is Tibby. You will have read all about me in my mum's (Tabby calls her Marnie), first book, *Nine Lives and One More*. It is all about my life with her and her family and after I left them to go to my heavenly home.

I was a stray, just like Tabby, looking for a home, but I did not have a friendly ghost-cat to help me, though perhaps I did have a Guardian Angel for, like Tabby, I certainly found the right home. I lived with my mum and her family for a long time until I became very ill and died. I remember that day so well. My mum stayed with me all through the previous night and then on the Friday morning I just fell 'asleep' in her arms. I was taken up to my new home in heaven. My mum was very sad when I left her and although I liked my new home very much and understood why I was there, I was sad for her. I could still see and hear her, but she couldn't see me except for a photograph that she kept by her bed. Nevertheless, she talked to me every day. I spoke to the other animals in heaven about this and I asked St Francis if there was anything I could do to ease my mum's grief. He suggested that I visit my mum on earth in the shape of a ghost-cat, but he warned me that some humans are frightened by an apparition. Most ghosts are friendly spirits and they can be helpful, but some are not nice. Humans are not sure which are good or bad, and because they do not understand about them they are often frightened or say that there are no such things as ghosts. Some humans say they can feel a 'presence' near them, specially when someone they love has died. This often helps them to come to terms with their loss. They have a warm feeling of someone or something watching over them and they don't feel quite so sad. I thought 'going back to earth' was a nice idea. I could come and go whenever I wanted to.

'Go when the moon is full,' said St Francis, 'then you will be able to see your way clearly, but be back in time for breakfast.'

I told my friends where I was going and they wished me good luck. Several nights later the moon was full and bright. There were no clouds in the dark sky and the stars twinkled brightly. I decided to go on my new adventure to see my mum.

The garden was still the same as I remembered. My mum had dug the flower beds, and her husband had mowed the lawn. The bird table was still there, but of course the birds were all in bed. The houses were all in darkness because the humans were all asleep. I heard a baby cry and a light flashed on in one house, but it soon went out and all was quiet. An eerie glow spread out from the street lights. Everything was still and silent. A spider was busy spinning a web across the bushes, and a fat worm put its head out of its hole and wriggled across my path.

'Hello,' I said, but he didn't answer.

Of course, the people and creatures of earth would not be able to see or hear me, except for a very few perceptive people who were more aware of our world. I wandered around the garden seeking out all my favourite old haunts. The holly tree was still there where I used to sit and hide waiting for a bird to hop near me. In heaven, of course, no creature hunts or hurts another. We all live together quite happily. One of my friends is a mouse and my best friends are three dogs that used to belong to my mum when she was a little girl. Lions and tigers, deer and antelope all graze together. People do not fight each other and no one is hungry. When will humans on earth learn to live like us? I looked around the garden. Everything looked the same.

'Hurry up,' whistled the wind. 'It will be daylight soon. The moon is going to bed and the sun will be up.'

'All right,' I said sadly, 'I am coming. Thank you for waiting for me.'

With a light puff of wind and a wink from the moon, I was soon back in my heavenly garden with my friends.

'What was it like?' they chorused together.

'Wonderful,' I replied, feeling a little dizzy. 'Everything looked the same.'

'Did you see your mum?' asked one of the animals.

'No,' I answered, 'she was asleep, but I might see her next time I go.'

After that I ate my breakfast, found a nice warm spot and went to sleep.

7

Turn Right Past the Milky Way

After that first visit, I went several times to earth. Once or twice I went in the daytime. Sometimes I saw my mum, but I knew she couldn't see me.

Once I brushed past her and I heard her say to her husband, 'Do you know, I almost thought Tibbs was in the garden, but it must have been a leaf that brushed my leg. Funny though, there doesn't seem to be a breeze.'

After that I often walked past her.

She couldn't see me but she smiled and said, 'I still think about you, little Tibbs, and I miss you. I hope you are all right.'

'Yes, I am mum,' I said, but she couldn't hear me.

Some days the back door was open so I crept in, and had a look around. Of course, it didn't matter whether the door was open or shut. That is the good thing about being a ghost-cat, I can get in and out of anywhere without having to wait for someone to open the door. Everything was in its place, even my own mat was still in my special feeding place. I sniffed around the secret places upstairs. I couldn't smell another cat, so I didn't think my mum had got one to replace me. There was a picture of me by her bed and a familiar picture of St Francis.

As I came down the stairs mum called out, 'Tibby,' and caught her breath. 'Oh no,' she said, 'I must be seeing things. I thought I saw Tibby, but of course it couldn't have been her. I will have to see about getting another cat. I will go to the Rescue Centre and find a little cat who needs a home and a lot of love.'

I felt happy to hear her say that. There are lots of cats who have no home or are unhappy where they are. Some are turned out, or badly treated by their owners. The Rescue Centre is very good and gives them food and shelter, but it is not like having a home of your own and someone to cuddle you. It was time for me to go back, but I felt happy so I purred for all I was worth.

'Here comes Tibby,' commented a gerbil. 'She looks like the cat who has just swallowed the cream. Swaggering along with her tail in the air.'

I sat in the sun in the heavenly gardens for some time and all my friends visited me to hear about my exploits.

One night I felt an overwhelming urge to visit earth. I wanted to stay where I was, but somehow I felt I must go. It was rather windy and some storm clouds were blowing up. With a jump I landed in the garden. I left so quickly that I had forgotten to have my supper. I felt a little hungry and just at that moment a mouse sauntered by.

'Here comes supper,' I said to myself.

I pounced, but I was most surprised to find I landed on the mouse with no effect.

'Of course, I am a ghost-cat,' I reminded myself. 'I will have to wait until I get back. Now why am I here?'

Suddenly I saw a bedraggled tabby cat sitting under a bush.

'Oh dear,' I said. 'Someone needs my help.' I crept up to the cat knowing that she could not see me. I whispered in the wind, 'Don't worry, little cat, I will help you.'

I kept a watch on her for a few days and realised that she did not have a home or anyone to look after her. Occassionally she was able to catch a bird, but she was not very good at it. She was not cleaning herself properly and she jumped and ran every time she heard a noise. The foxes were prowling around and she seemed afraid of them. They could sense that I was there and so they quickly moved off to their old shed.

Well, you know what happened next. She sneaked into the garage and got stuck up in the roof. I kept telling her to jump down, but she was too frightened and wouldn't listen to me. When my mum got her down after three days, she ran away as fast as she could. Later that night she calmed down and went to sleep. I stayed close by. The next day she hung around the garden and I could tell she was very hungry and miserable. I had to do something, so I miaowed with all my might. I saw her ears prick up.

'Come on little cat,' I said softly, 'the lady will look after you and feed you. Go and miaow outside the back door. She has been waiting for a little cat like you to love.'

I am sure she heard me, because she walked down the path miaowing. My mum heard her and came out and fed her. It was love at first sight, though I knew my mum would never forget me.

'Thank you Tibby for sending Tabitha,' I heard her say as she looked towards where I was sitting, but I know she couldn't really see me.

Tabitha, what a mouthful. I am glad they shortened it to Tabby. All of a sudden I was very tired, so I decided it was time to go home. I told my friends all about my adventure and they all thought I had been very kind and thoughtful. I must say I felt pleased for the little cat and my mum. I don't think I shall need to visit earth quite so much now. I think they will sort themselves out.

Sweet dreams, Tabby. Be happy in your new home.

8

Mice, Birds and a Piece of Wool

It took me some time to settle down in my new home. There were lots of new noises that I had to get used to, like the central heating banging as the boiler came on. When it did I made a sudden bolt for the door; the door bell ringing or the telephone and I made myself, very scarce when anyone was using the hoover.

'It's all right, Tabby, I am here,' said Marnie, trying to calm me down. 'Nothing will hurt you.'

At the weekend, Marnie had a lie-in and her husband got up first. I was usually hungry by the time he came down, so when he put my bowl of food down, I gobbled it up quickly and was ready for a second helping. Then I liked to go out into the garden and have a sniff around. There were a lot of birds at the bird table and the noise was deafening as they fought to get onto the feeders. I liked to sit under the picnic table and keep an eye on them. Sometimes a sparrow came quite close and I got ready to pounce. If Marnie saw me she waved the curtain so that the bird flew away into the holly tree. The birds sat in the tree chattering until they thought it was safe to go back to the feeders. Although I kept myself well hidden, I think they knew I was around. As soon as I went indoors they flew down to the ground and started to hunt for crumbs.

One day I caught a small bird and held it carefully in my mouth. It was very still so I thought it was dead. Some people dislike cats because they catch mice and birds, not because they are hungry, but just to play with them. Often it is the well-fed cat that stalks a prey, because, for one thing, it is the healthy cat who has enough energy for the chase, whereas a neglected cat although hungry does not have all its strength. It is a primeval instinct inherited from our ancestors when they were wild animals and had to depend on what they caught to survive. Lions and tigers in their particular wild habitat stalk other animals because their lives and those of their families depend on it. Most humans don't mind a cat catching mice. In fact cats are often kept for that purpose, on farms or in grain stores. Humans don't understand: mice or birds, they are all the same to us. The instinct inherited from our forebears is still with us. I carried the bird gently in my mouth and put it down on the grass, but quick as a flash it flew away, a little unsteady at first. I hunted around everywhere. I looked behind the dustbin, but it had gone. I couldn't believe it. I used to be good at catching birds when there was nothing else to eat.

A few days later I was pursuing a mouse that lived under the garage floor. A black cat from down the road often sat near the doors for hours waiting for the mouse to appear. I was sitting by the back door when I saw a movement. I scampered after it. It was the mouse. I caught hold of him in my mouth. Mice are wily creatures. They make out they are dead in the hope that the predator will drop them. I laid him down but put a paw on his tail. He did not move, but just then something else took my attention for a second, and he was off and running for his life across the lawn. The chase was on but he crawled under a brick. I knew he was there but I couldn't reach him. I sniffed all around and finally got my paws under the brick and grabbed him. I only wanted to play with him. Marnie shut the back door quickly.

'Don't bring that mouse in here,' she yelled hysterically.

She stood by the window watching while I played with him. I threw him up in the air several times until he didn't seem to have any life left in him. I got fed up and put him down, but I kept an eye on him. As I said you never know with a mouse. They may just be playing 'dead'. Very slowly he started to creep away. I followed him with my nose to the ground ready to pounce. Suddenly he disappeared into the flower beds. I hunted around, jumping over flowers, sniffing and pawing the ground. Once or twice I saw him and gave chase, but after a long time I had to give up as I was worn to a whisker. The mouse had won the day and I was very cross, so I went indoors to sulk.

'Next time, mouse, I will get you,' I muttered to myself.

I walked slowly up the stairs to bed.

'I think that mouse has got nine lives,' said Marnie laughing.

'Hmm,' I said under my breath, 'he will only have eight next time.'

Since I have been in my new home I get my meals regularly every day. Sometimes there are cat treats and crunched up biscuits with my Whiskas. The vet said I am a fat cat, but now that I get good food at proper times, I am bound to fill out a bit and I am not fond of too much exercise. This is the life: sleep, eat and bird/mouse watch in the garden. There is a choice of three beds and I don't know how many armchairs. It is funny, though. When I want to sleep on my favourite chair, the man is always there. He says it is his chair, but if I get there first, it is *my* chair.

The other day Marnie was knitting, she knits teddy bears for charity, and she dropped a piece of wool on the floor. I sniffed it and it got stuck in my mouth. I thought it was something to eat. Marnie grabbed me, but I had got it inside my mouth. I gulped and down it went.

'She has swallowed it,' shouted Marnie to the man.

'Oh dear,' he replied anxiously, 'perhaps she will be sick and bring it up.'

I wasn't sick. In fact I felt very good. I had my supper and went to bed. The next day Marnie phoned the vet and told him what had happened.

'Is it dangerous?' she asked.

'Yes,' replied the vet, 'you must watch her very carefully.

If she is sick or has diarrhoea, you must bring her to the surgery immediately and we will investigate what is going on inside her. It might mean an operation to find out where the piece of wool is. It might pass through her then all will be well. You must keep her in for three or four days, but if you are not happy about her condition don't hesitate to bring her in.'

'Oh dear,' sighed Marnie, 'that won't be easy keeping her in, but I will do my best. Thank you.'

Of course, I miaowed at the back door to be let out, but Marnie wouldn't let me go. As soon as I heard the keys being rattled, I ran to the kitchen but Marnie was very careful. There was nothing to do but sleep and eat and watch the world go by from the window sill.

All day Monday I tried to get out into the garden, but Marnie was wise to my efforts. Tuesday was the same. I got lots of love and kisses and food, but the door stayed shut. On Wednesday the plumber was coming to look at the central heating.

'I had better shut puss in the front room,' said Marnie. 'She won't like that, I know.'

There was a knock at the front door. Marnie went to open it.

'Allo, I'm 'Arry the plumber and this 'ere is me mate, Justin. Jus fer short. We're 'ere to look at yer pipes – central 'eating.'

'Oh – er – yes,' stammered Marnie a little taken aback. 'Hmm, of course, come in.' Marnie shut the door and showed them the 'pipes'. 'Er, would you both like a cup of tea or something before you start?'

'Yus tar, a nice cuppa "Rosie Lee" will go down jes right, won't it Jus? Milk, three sugars, tar,' said Harry in his gruff Cockney voice.

'Oh, could I have coff-ee,' piped up Justin. 'Black, no sugar, thanks love.'

Just then I walked out of the front room into the kitchen.

'Oh, look, you have a pussy cat,' commented Justin and tweaked my tail.

‘’Ere, we aint ’ere to play wiv the cat,’ uttered Harry. ‘Shin up that ladder and be quick abowt it.’

Justin’s blond, out of a hairdresser’s bottle, head disappeared into the trapdoor that led to the loft. His somewhat slim body lost in a pair of workman’s dirty dungarees followed.

‘Oh – er – it’s ever so dark up here,’ said the disembodied voice of Justin. ‘Have you got a candle?’

‘No,’ said Marnie trying to stifle a giggle, ‘but there is a light switch to your left.’

‘Oh, that’s much better,’ came the voice. ‘It’s like Aladdin’s cave. I bet you have got some treasures up here.’

‘No,’ replied Marnie now almost hysterical with laughter, ‘none that *The Antiques Roadshow* would value.’

Her husband gave her a dig in the ribs and she rushed into the kitchen on the pretence of a coughing fit.

I retreated into the front room and sat on the window sill. I heard the man come into the kitchen.

‘Hello Harry,’ he said, ‘got a new mate I see. Is he any good?’

‘Yus,’ reflected Harry, chewing on a biscuit with the two or three yellowing teeth left in his mouth, ‘not bad. I can’t get up them there ladders anymore, not like I ust to. ’Ee’s abit posh for this job, but as long as ’ee does what I tells ’im, that’s okey-dokey by me. ’Ee works in one of them there cocker-tail bars in the h-evenings. Finks ’ees a wow wiv the ladies. Watch out, Missus, ’ee’ll be givin’ you the eye. No offence lady, only kiddin’.’

‘None taken,’ said Marnie rather sharply.

‘Fred said you’ve ’ad some trouble wiv yer old ticker. Bad wos it?’ inquired Harry of the man. ‘Otherwise you’d be shinning up that ladder yerself.’

‘Yes,’ answered the man, ‘have to be careful now as to what I can and can’t do.’

‘Oh, what a shame,’ commented Justin. ‘We never know what is just around the corner do we?’

‘Jest as well,’ said Harry under his breath. ‘Come on, Jus, can’t ’ang abowt gassing all day. Work to be done, lad. Time is money, son, time is money. Fanks fer the rosie-lee, Missus.'

Marnie shut me in the front room with a bowl of water, some biscuits and my litter tray. I heard voices outside talking and laughing. Then Harry came in to test the radiators. He left the sliding door open, so I sidled out and, heavens, the back door was open where he had put a rubber hose out to drain the water from the pipes. I squeezed through the opening and smelt the fresh air.

'The cat has escaped,' yelled Marnie's husband.

'Oh no,' screamed Marnie, 'catch her quick, but go carefully and slowly otherwise she will run when she sees you.'

I saw him out of the corner of my eye. He was closing in on one side and Marnie on the other. Harry was standing at the back door.

'Sorry,' he said apologetically, wiping his hands on a greasy cloth that had probably begun life as a handkerchief, and lifted his even greasier cloth cap to scratch his semi-bald head. His steel-rimmed glasses were so scratched and smeared that it was a wonder he could see a hand in front of his face. He put the dirty cloth back into his pocket and proceeded to wipe his oily hands on his ill-fitting and similarly dirty work jacket and trousers. The buttons were hanging off and his large beer belly hung over the top of his trousers, now almost at half mast.

'I ditn't know 'ee wasn't allowed awt.'

'It's not your fault,' answered Marnie, creeping towards me. I made a sudden dash down the garden, as I knew I could outrun both of them. Marnie walked along the path shaking the biscuit tin.

'Come on Tabby,' she called, 'biscuits.'

I did not fall for that old trick. I was wise to Marnie. If I stopped to eat a biscuit, she would grab me and before I knew it I would be indoors and the back door shut tight. I dived under the hedge, but, wouldn't you know, it started to rain and I got soaking wet. At first, I thought I would stay and brave it out, but my coat got wetter and wetter, my ears drooped and the rain dripped off my nose, so I decided I had better go back to the house. At least it was warm and dry indoors.

'Cat's coming back,' shouted Harry, looking very relieved.

'Keep quiet and don't move,' Marnie whispered back, 'and when she is in give her some biscuits and shut the door quick.'

'Oh, so you have decided to come back, have you,' exclaimed Marnie's husband quietly. 'Good puss, come and have some biscuits.'

'Oh well,' I thought, 'better luck next time.'

'Oh you are a nice pussy cat,' interrupted Justin and tweaked my tail again.

Next day, Thursday, after I had used my litter tray, Marnie said, 'You are a very good puss. You are all better now, so you can go out into the garden. We won't have to take you to the vet now.'

The back door opened and I skipped out into the sunshine. I sat under the holly tree and wondered what all the fuss was about.

A few weeks later I did not feel very well. My jaw hurt, especially when I ate my food. I couldn't eat my biscuits as my teeth felt very sore. I really felt 'under the weather', so after I had eaten some of my breakfast, I went upstairs to Sally's bed and stayed there all day. Marnie was alarmed and said she didn't think I was very well. The man had said the day before that he thought my breath smelt nasty. Tuesday, I felt the same. I slept most of the day, but I did manage to eat some of my fish in the evening. Marnie rang the vet and made an appointment for the next day. Out came the wire basket and off we went. A nice young lady carefully prodded me and took my temperature.

'Well, I can't find anything wrong,' she said, stroking me, 'but she has got a bad tooth, which needs to come out. Bring her back next week and we will sort it out. That is what is probably making her feel so poorly.'

'Thank you,' replied Marnie holding me gently. 'Will you make the appointment for next Thursday. What do I have to do?'

'She must not have anything to eat after 5 o'clock the day before, and you must bring her to the surgery between 8.00 and 8.30 a.m.' explained the vet.

'That's not as easy as it sounds,' murmured Marnie quietly, 'but we will manage it somehow.'

The next day I felt a little brighter, but I noticed there were no biscuits on my plate and Marnie had mashed up the food for me.

Wednesday and all seemed to be going well, as far as I was concerned. Little did I know that Marnie was in a state of anxiety. She cooked my fish as usual, though it did seem a bit early, and she sat with me while I ate it, encouraging me to eat all of it. With my tummy full I went off to bed. At about 7.00 p.m., my usual supper time, I came down to see where it was. I walked around Marnie and her husband and miaowed loudly, but nobody took any notice.

'I can't feed you, puss,' said Marnie sorrowfully, 'and you have had your fish.'

I had never heard Marnie say things like that before. Oh well, I still felt full up with fish, so I went off to have another sleep. At 10 o'clock I tried again, but the same thing happened. No amount of cajoling on my part got me any food. I rolled over and tried all the tricks I knew, but all to no avail.

'It is a good job you are a fat puss, Tabby. That will keep you going for a while,' remarked Marnie.

I didn't think that was a very nice comment to make, but she didn't mean to be unkind. All the lights went out and there was nothing for it but to go back to bed.

The next morning the birds woke me up around 5.00 a.m., so I went off in search of someone to give me some food. Usually it was the man who got up to feed me, but the bedroom door was open so I went in and walked all over Marnie, but she just stroked me and turned over, so I tried the man and he did the same. An hour later Marnie got up. I waited patiently outside the bathroom door until she came out, then I followed her down the stairs and sat in my place by her chair and waited for my breakfast. Marnie sat down with hers and looked at me sadly.

'I can't give you anything to eat, puss,' she said, 'not until your tooth is better.'

I didn't understand what she meant, though my tooth did hurt when I ate my food and my jaw ached. I walked round and round her feet purring, rolling over for attention which I got but not my Whiskas. Marnie had got a bit crafty of late. She brought the wire basket down and hid it so that I wouldn't see it, then all of a sudden she got hold of me and put me into it whilst she talked to me and told me I would soon feel better. Didn't she know I would feel a lot better with some food inside me? A strange car pulled up outside the front door and Marnie put me on the back seat, then got in next to me and off we went. I miaowed most of the way because I was hungry. Marnie kept telling me that soon my tooth would be better and I would be back home with all the food I could eat. At the surgery she handed me over to a lady in a blue uniform.

'One nervous cat and one traumatised owner,' she announced.

The lady in blue, a veterinary nurse, took me into a large room. There were other cats in boxes and baskets, all of them making a lot of noise. One Oriental-looking cat made an awful high-pitched wailing sound. I decided to be brave as I was sure Marnie wouldn't leave me unless it was for my own good. After a while most of the other cats had quietened down, except for the Siamese, who really did have a piercing cry. The nurse came back and took the cats out one by one. Soon it was my turn. She took me into a strange room where the light was very bright. There were one or two other people in long white coats standing about. The nurse took me out of my wire basket and put me onto a table. She held onto me very tightly but she talked softly to me and stroked my head. One of the other people put a needle in me and suddenly I felt very sleepy. I couldn't keep my eyes open.

When I woke up, I was back in my wire basket with all

the other cats in their baskets, etc. All of them seemed to be asleep, even the Siamese. I must say I was glad of that. The nurse came in and spoke to each one of us in turn. My jaw still ached a bit, but it felt different from before, then she came and picked up my basket and took me outside and there was Marnie. I knew she wouldn't leave me forever.

'She has recovered well,' the nurse told Marnie, 'but keep her indoors for about 48 hours while the anaesthetic works through her. Give her soft food mashed up for a while.'

'I've got fish tonight, is that all right,' asked Marnie, 'and Whiskas tomorrow?'

'Yes,' replied the nurse, 'and don't worry if she doesn't want to eat tonight. Her jaw will be sore for a time.'

The man was waiting outside in the car and he seemed pleased to see me. When we got home Marnie cooked some fish and gave it to me in small portions. I suddenly realised how hungry I was and I ate it all. About an hour later, I asked Marnie for some Whiskas and she gave me three lots.

'I don't know,' exclaimed Marnie laughing, 'the nurse said you might not want to eat and here you are eating me out of house and home.'

My legs felt a bit wobbly, but I managed to climb slowly up the stairs to bed.

The next day things got back to normal.

I did ask to go out once or twice, but I wasn't bothered too much when Marnie said, 'Not today, Tabitha.'

Hmm. I must be special if she calls me Tabitha. Is it my birthday? My jaw was still a bit sore, but after a time it felt better and I soon forgot all about it. At least it didn't stop me eating. By Saturday I was back to my old self again. I didn't like the experience, but I knew Marnie only did it for my good. I didn't hold it against her, though next time I hope she doesn't stop feeding me.

9

Home Sweet Home

I don't think about my old home any more. In fact I hardly ever go out of the garden. There is plenty to explore, especially in the wild places, and there are lots of birds to watch. This is my home now. I am given plenty of food and there are lots of warm places to sleep in or sunbathe. I can have a different 'bed' every day of the week if I choose, but I have my favourite places and one or two secret ones. My best evening 'bed' is the man's chair. It is often a race as to who gets there first – him or me. If he gets there first I stalk around his feet and stare at him, then as soon as he gets up I jump on. The seat is nice and warm.

'Puss,' he says in a pretend cross voice, 'you have taken my seat.'

If I sit on the settee, he sits next to me and strokes my head. I pretend to be fast asleep. Marnie knows the nature of a cat and leaves me alone when I want to sleep or be by myself, but the man likes to stroke my paws. If I wag my tail Marnie scolds him.

'She wants to be left alone,' she says sharply.

We seem to have settled into a nice routine. The man gets up early to feed me and then goes back to bed while I sit by the window and watch the birds. Marnie gets up about 8 o'clock and has a shower. While she has her breakfast, she gives me some more Whiskas and after that I go out into the garden if I want to. I can just about wait until then to do a 'wee', but there is always a litter tray in case I get taken 'short'. When I come back in I go upstairs to sleep again, but if Marnie and the man are going out, she shuts the back door and locks it.

'That's it, Tabby,' she says, 'you can't go out any more until we come home.'

She doesn't like me to stay out if there is no one at home, because she knows I am still rather nervous of noises and other animals and she doesn't want me to go off and get lost. So I have to stay in and find a nice warm place to sleep until they come home. If they are going to be out for some time Marnie leaves me a bowl of biscuits, but I don't bother with them unless I am really hungry. When they return home again she opens the back door and I am free to do as I please. Marnie was a little concerned that I seem to sleep a lot during the day, but I often stay awake and alert most of the night. I suppose I got used to it when I was living rough. One has to be alert especially in the dark in case of other enemies. Most days she and the man are at home, so I am not restricted as to where I can go. I like to wander round and sniff the bushes or sit in my favourite place and watch for birds or mice. There is a black and white cat that comes into the garden now and then. He wears a collar so he must have a home, but he likes to tease the birds and will eat up anything that Marnie has put out for them. Some cats are scavengers whether or not they are well fed. If I see him I chase him off before Marnie sees him in case she feels sorry for him. She is a 'push-over' for anything with four legs. Marnie says I am very good because I dig all my holes (well, nearly all) in our garden. Some cats always leave their mess in someone else's garden, especially if it is nice and tidy and newly dug over. It is easier to dig a hole if the earth is soft. That is why some people don't like cats, particularly if their garden is their pride and joy. But Marnie doesn't mind. She loves her garden and I think she is very good at growing things, but she has also made it habitable for a cat. I come in for my food, but in summer I go out for hours. I have a secret place in the next-door garden which nobody knows about except me. Not even Marnie knows where it really is. In the late evening she calls and calls but I only come when I am ready. As the evenings start to get colder and I feel hungry, I show myself.

'Come in,' says Marnie, 'the foxes will get you and have you for their supper.'

I would like to see them try, my claws are very sharp.

I have had my mad moments, but I don't play as much as I used to. I am very happy and contented with my new family and I know I am a very lucky cat. Not all animals are so well looked after. Some humans are very cruel because they think that 'dumb' animals can't feel or think, but they can and if someone is being cruel or unkind it hurts the animal just the same as if it were a person being hurt. Children don't mean to be unkind, but kittens and puppies are small and fragile and should be handled carefully. Every animal likes to be loved and tries to please their owners even when they are not treated kindly. Animals are very loyal creatures, especially dogs and horses. Cats have a mind of their own, and if they are very unhappy they will try to find another home or fend for themselves, but lots of other creatures can't do that. They have to stay in the place where they are put, however sad or hurt they may feel. Lions and tigers are sometimes put into cages which are too small for them and dolphins and whales are confined for amusement in pleasure parks, whereas they should be roaming the open seas. Birds in a small cage or goldfish in a tiny bowl is just as cruel. Some humans just don't think what they are doing to the creatures.

Marnie has become a 'container gardener'. Since the garden was landscaped recently, she has done away with a lot of the flower beds, to make it easier for herself.

'I am not getting any younger, puss,' she confided to me one day.

She says she loves gardening but her back doesn't. So although there are still some small plots for flowers and vegetables, and a very large lawn, she has lots of pots and containers dotted around the garden. In winter she put them near the house or in her potting shed to protect them from the weather. She calls herself an amateur gardener, but I think she is very good. Her friend said she had got 'green fingers', but they didn't look green to me. Well, anyway, she put lots of pots with spring bulbs in near the house and two square containers that didn't look as if there was anything growing in them. In fact one did have something in it and the other just had compost in it ready for planting. The other day she put netting over the square boxes to stop the squirrels or foxes from digging in them. She had seen footprints in one of them, but I have to confess it was my paw print. I like to sit on the outside window ledge behind the containers and sometimes I take a short cut over the boxes if I am in a hurry to get back indoors. Yesterday I was sitting on the ledge when I suddenly had the urge to do a 'wee'. There was no time to hunt around under the holly tree for a convenient spot, so as the earth in the box was newly dug, I decided to use that. I put my two back paws up on top of either side and my two front paws on the front side with my tail up in the air. At that moment Marnie came out of the house and saw me. She stood for a while till I had finished, then she said a naughty word, two in fact.

'Tabby, I have just planted my new lily bulbs in there. They cost me £7,' she said, half-laughing, half-cross. 'They are my lily containers, not your private loo.' She ran in to tell her husband. 'I don't know,' she said. 'I have to wage war on slugs and snails, on vine weevils, squirrels and foxes, and now it's Tabby spending a "penny" on my prize lilies. I thought gardening would be a nice gentle occupation for my retirement, instead I find it is like fighting World War Three.'

I walked in calmly and went to bed.

I saw the 'grey cat' last evening. We talked for some time, and she said she would not be coming to earth any more unless I was in trouble. She was very happy where she is and has lots of friends. She was happy for Marnie (mum), because now she had me and she doesn't cry for Tibby, though she still talks to her and has a photo of her by her bed. The 'grey cat' said I was to be good to Marnie and not stay out all hours and worry her.

'There are windows in heaven,' said the grey cat solemnly, 'and I can look through whenever I want to and see you and Mum.'

We talked some more, then there was a puff of wind and she was gone. I looked up at the moon and I am sure it winked at me. Time to go in. Marnie will be waiting.

'Goodnight, Tibby Grey Cat. See you again some day.'

10

Trespassers Will Be...

One day a small ginger cat came into the garden. He sniffed around under the holly tree and other places. I was sitting inside the back door and it was open just enough for me to squeeze through. He looked younger and more energetic than me and as he was much smaller than me, I did not feel threatened, but I did not want him in *my* garden. I crept out cautiously, then I ran at him spitting and snarling. I didn't really mean it but it sounded menacing. He ran off down the garden as fast as he could go with me in hot pursuit. For all my extra weight I can still run or jump when I need to. Of course, he was more agile than I was, but I kept going. I chased after him down the garden path as fast as I could, but he ran behind the garage and vanished. I looked around angrily, but I could not see where he had gone. I had lost him. Marnie, who had been watching from the kitchen, shouted at me but I took no notice. She did not want me to get into a fight. Soon she gave up calling me and shut the back door. I walked determinedly all around looking for the ginger cat. I did not want to have a fight, just to scare him off my territory. There was a high wall at the end of the fence, so I jumped up onto the fence and then onto the wall. Once I was up there it looked a long way down to the ground. The ginger cat was nowhere to be seen. I wobbled a bit as I walked carefully up and down on the top of the wall. I began to miaow loudly. Marnie heard me and rushed out.

'Oh dear, puss,' she exclaimed, 'now you are in a fine fix. Wait a moment and I will get some steps and see if I can reach you.'

She ran indoors just as the man came out of the garage.

'What are you doing up there?' he said, staring up in amazement.

By now I had become quite frightened. The ground below was concrete and looked hard. I tried all ways to get down. I began to get alarmed. The man stretched up to me, but he was unable to reach me. Just as Marnie came back with the steps I panicked and jumped down.

'Ouch,' my toes tingled but I was all right.

I must remember not to go up there again. I wondered where the ginger cat had gone.

'He had better not come back,' I muttered between clenched teeth.

I liked to sit and watch the birds through the wire fence between the gardens. There were lots of trees and bushes on the other side, but near to the house there was a wooden fence as high as the wall. There were overgrown flower beds on the other side of the fence and the earth was soft. I found I could scramble up the fence and jump over, or I could walk right along the top of the fence into the holly tree. I could see the birds in the tree, but as soon as I began to get near they started to make a lot of noise and all flew away. Marnie saw me up on the fence and banged on the window, but I jumped over into the next-door garden. I had not been in there since my days of being homeless. I sniffed around keeping an eye open for other animals. As this was not my territory I had to be careful. The scents and smells were all different and strange to me. After a while I lost interest. I managed to jump up onto the top of the fence and over onto our plastic dustbin. From there I could jump to the picnic table, which in winter Marnie kept covered. I sat on it and licked my fur for a while. Marnie did not like me going on these exploits because she didn't want me to be chased by a dog or get lost, but she knew she could not stop me and I was very, very careful because I did not want to get lost either.

Now that summer had ended the nights were drawing in and the weather had become colder. The radiators in the house were switched on and I could feel the warmth from them if I sat near to them. The one in the dining room was right next to Marnie's chair. I sat with my nose right up against it.

'Try getting a little nearer, puss,' said Marnie, laughing.

So I did. I sat on top of it, but it wasn't very comfortable, so I settled down beside it again and the warmth lulled me to sleep. My favourite place in winter is on the big armchair, Marnie and the man bought a new three-piece suite. They said it cost an 'arm and a leg'. Funny, it looked like a settee and two armchairs to me. The man had a special chair just for himself. It is called a 'recliner'. I liked that chair best of all. I often slept on it in the evenings. It is also near the radiator, so I can get the 'best of both worlds'.

'How much money did we spend on that chair?' Marnie remarked one evening. 'And now you can't sit on it because puss has taken it over.'

The man was very kind and didn't disturb me if I got there before him. During the day I liked to sleep on the top of it, but the man said it would make the back go a peculiar shape and spoil the armchair, so he put a newspaper on it so that I couldn't sit up there, but sometimes Marnie took pity on me and removed the paper, then I could creep up and have a nice sleep. I spend a lot of my time sleeping. Marnie thinks that is why I am so fat. In summer, I don't mind going outside, but in winter, brr... Indoors is the best place for a contented cat.

I like a lot of fuss, and I like my back rubbed, then I roll over and let them rub my tummy. Marnie likes to pick me up, but I am not too happy about that. I know Marnie and the man would not hurt me, but I am not used to being picked up. Tibby used to sit on Marnie's lap for ages, and I know she wishes I would, but she respects that I don't feel comfortable, so she holds me for a little while and when I start to struggle she puts me down. The only time I will really let her hold me is first thing in the morning. When I hear her getting up I bound up the stairs, miaowing loudly and talking, then she picks me up and carries me downstairs, talking back to me while I nuzzle into her face. After a few minutes she puts me down and gives me my breakfast. They are getting quite good at interpreting cat language, as they seem to understand what I want. The other morning while they were both still in bed, I yowled very loudly. Marnie had got up at 6 o'clock to give me my breakfast, but then she went back to bed for a couple of hours.

'She can't be hungry again,' Marnie said to the man, yawning her head off.

'No,' replied the man still half-asleep, 'she wants to go outside. I'll go down and open the back door.'

'Why won't she use the litter tray?' questioned Marnie and then turned over and went back to sleep.

When we got downstairs it was raining.

'It's raining cats and dogs,' commented the man. 'Do you really want to go out in that?'

I couldn't see any cats or dogs, but I wanted to go so bad that I just ran underneath the holly tree and did my 'business' then raced back indoors.

'Phew,' muttered the man still half-asleep, 'that was quick. You don't waste time doing it, do you? I hope you are not wet. It is not really the best time of day to sit and dry you off.'

He felt my fur and it was not very wet, so off he went back to bed. Marnie got up again about 8 o'clock and gave me another bowl of Whiskas. I finished it all up and went off to bed.

The other day I caught another mouse. This time it was a large one. I carried it gently in my mouth into the garden. Marnie saw me coming, so she screamed and shut the back door quickly. I put it down on the lawn.

'Now for a game,' I said to myself.

I looked away and the mouse moved, so I put my paw on

its tail. We played this game for a while, but the mouse was very cunning. He made out he was dead, so that I would lose interest, but I knew he was only pretending. Then, with a sideways glance, he was off into the flower beds. I chased after it, but he was quick and darted behind some boxes. Eventually he managed to hide in a corner behind the dust-bins. I could not reach him. I tried every which way to get to him, but it was no use. I sat and glared at him hoping to frighten him, but Sally, who was visiting, picked me up and took me indoors.

'Leave the poor thing alone, it's smaller than you,' she said laughing. 'You are a big, fat bully, but we all love you.'

'I'll get it the next time I go out,' I said menacingly, but they wouldn't let me go out any more, so I sat and ate a whole tin of tuna, then went to bed and sulked. 'I'll get it tomorrow, you see if I don't.'

Next morning I was up at the 'crack of dawn', well when the humans got up. I miaowed to be let out, even before I had had any breakfast. I hunted around, but there was no sign of the mouse. All of a sudden I saw something big, bigger than a mouse and almost as big as me, up on the top of the high wall. It didn't look like a cat as it had a big bushy tail and a sharp nose. It was running along the wall, this way and that. I stared nervously at it.

'My,' I thought, 'that mouse has grown a lot overnight.'

Marnie saw it and got very excited.

'A squirrel,' she shouted. 'Look it has come to eat the nuts on the bird table, but it can see the cat.'

'What,' yelled the man, 'a squirrel? That's all I need.'

He was having a lot of trouble with pigeons and magpies frightening off all the smaller birds. 'I don't want a plague of squirrels as well.'

'It's hardly a plague,' replied Marnie, 'It's only one. Tabby has seen it and she is chasing after it, but I don't think there is much chance of her catching it.'

I ran as quickly as I could, but it was too fast for me. It disappeared over the back fence before I could get my second wind.

'I bet it will be back,' Marnie said, 'now that it knows where there is a "grocery store".'

Hmm. All the excitement was too much for me. I went back indoors for my breakfast and a sleep.

I have been here for four years now and things haven't changed much. The garden has been all sorted out and a lot of my hiding places have gone, but the holly tree is still there, so I can still lie in wait for the birds and I have found some nice new places. The garden looks very nice and Marnie and the man work hard in it. I like to be out in the garden when Marnie is out there working. In the morning she goes down and opens her potting shed door.

'Come on, puss, come for a walk down the garden with me,' she says.

I follow on behind and sniff all the plants, then I roll over and she tickles me. The man was in hospital for two weeks so now Marnie gets up early and gives me my breakfast every morning. I could get the man up any time of night by a miaow or a tap with my paw, but Marnie is more difficult to wake up. I have tried walking all over her at 5 o'clock in the morning and sitting on her chest, but she doesn't move. In fact she lies so still that I don't think she is asleep. She is pretending, because when the man was in hospital I slept with her for a couple of nights, but she snored so loudly that I didn't get a wink of sleep and when I did she twisted and turned so much that she nearly knocked me off the bed. So how is it that when I want to wake her up, she lies so still and quiet. These humans can be very crafty when they want to. I have got my own bed downstairs where no one can disturb me. Nevertheless, I don't sleep much at night. I prefer to be on guard, watching to see who is about in the dark. If I see a fox my tail bristles, though I know I am safe indoors, but I like to keep watch in case any mice or birds decide to invade the house while Marnie and her husband are asleep. Of course, the birds don't get up until daybreak, but the mice often scamper about in the dark and Marnie screams when she sees a mouse, so I have to defend her. With my sharp eyes I can see them running under the flower pots. If I were allowed out I could catch every one of them. One day a heron landed on the roof of the garage. Marnie ran to the window.

'Oh, isn't it beautiful,' she cried excitedly.

She usually only says that about me. She watched him as he flew to a nearby pond and proceeded to catch and eat the fish that were in there. Then he lifted up into the air and flew away. At times our garden is like a wildlife park. There is the squirrel who runs all over the garden looking for nuts that the birds have dropped. A robin that comes to perch on a branch when Marnie is digging. The magpies and pigeons that march around as if they owned the garden, and the starlings and sparrows that fight and squabble amongst themselves. Sometimes I wonder if there is any peace and quiet anywhere, so the best place is bed. The other day I heard two cats fighting, so I ran and hid under the bed. Marnie came to find me.

'It's all right, Tabby, you are quite safe with us,' she told me gently, trying to reach me and stroke my head.

That is what the 'grey cat' would have said. I often look out of the window into the garden to see if 'Tibby-grey-cat' is around. Sometimes I catch Marnie looking too. She has a wistful look in her eyes, but then she sees me.

'Fish for tea, Tabby,' she says and all is well.

This is my home and Marnie and the man love me just as much as they did Tibby, though Marnie says she will never forget her. Neither will I.

Goodbye 'Grey Cat'.

Thank you for guiding me here.

Song to the Grey Cat

When the moon is full and the stars are bright
And the wind blows softly through the trees,
Then the grey cat comes creeping step by step,
Unnoticed by all she sees.

Her eyes glow bright in the dark, dark night
And her whiskers quiver and twitch.
She glides silently by under a moonlit sky
And nobody sees her but me.

EPILOGUE

Easter 2000

Marnie is doing it again. A little black cat has started to come into the garden and take shelter in her small seed greenhouse. She puts a bowl of food out twice a day and told me that I wouldn't miss a little of my Whiskas as I don't eat a whole tin in any case. Someone said Marnie is a 'soft touch' and I agree with them!

When I am indoors and awake, I stare at the cat through the window. I think I frightened it a bit. Once I was in the garden when it came over the fence, so I chased it, but it was quicker than me and thinner, so it got away. Marnie thinks it has got a home, but maybe looking for a second one, or perhaps is shut out during the day so comes to us for food and shelter. Her friend says the neighbourhood cats know where 'the suckers live', but Marnie doesn't seem to mind. She says it is down to me whether or not I want to make friends with the Black Cat.

What would you say, Tibby 'Grey-Cat'? I think I know the answer to that question.